THANK YOU FROM A GRATEFUL HEART

A Woman's Journal to Capturing God's Heart Through Gratitude

LaShonda Lee

In Memory of my loving mother
Sherry Ann Hill

How Gratitude Changed My Life - My Story

After college, I got a job in the field of Social Work. I was blessed to master the art of serving my community and eventually opened up my own social service agency, hired staff and continued to work with individuals & families experiencing despair. Life was great because my agency was touching and improving the lives of many individuals and families, and as a result, it afforded my family a decent income and time freedom. This was important because it provided me the necessary freedom needed as a wife and a mother. Life was great and suddenly; my world was turned upside down. Due to me relying on government contracts, I found myself affected by some major financial cutbacks on the federal level, which trickled down to the state level. As a result of downsizing, my agency lost its contract. Just like that 100% of my personal and business income ended abruptly! I tried everything I knew to do to maintain, but nothing materialized. I was not able to pick up the pieces and I found myself in a place I had never been before. I was fearful, stressed, discouraged, angry, hurt, sad, confused, scared, and hopeless. Everything I had worked for had been stripped away. My income was gone, I lost my home and vehicles were repossessed. I went from living in a 3-story home to a small bedroom in my mother's home with my son. On top of that, my husband and I at the time divorced. For a while, my internal conversation was one of failure. My internal conversation screamed "I failed at my business", I failed at my marriage" and the most hurt was feeling like failed at being a parent. This mental and emotional anguish accompanied me every day for a couple of years. I felt this was a sign that I wasn't worthy of having lasting success, happiness, and fulfillment. I believed I made to many mistakes in the past and this was my well-deserved punishment...maybe you can relate.

Again, I would love to tell you I shook it off and bounced right back; however, I can't. My life was in shambles and I didn't want to exist in it anymore! One bad life experience and it's easy to slip into depression. I consistently looked at the glass half-empty and worried about everything that could go wrong.

Weeping may endure for the night, but I promise joy comes in the morning. It was at this point I was introduced to a young lady that help change the trajectory of my life. I wasn't moving past my pain was that I was using my imagination negatively. I was focused on my past hurts and pains instead of the blessing that was before me called "opportunity". Through her teaching and coaching, I was introduced to the concept of gratitude. She said "LaShonda, anytime you get into a depressed state, gratitude has the power to shift your mood immediately. To be honest, I didn't feel like being grateful, I wanted to wallow in my pain and continue to share my victim story.

It took some time, but one day I asked myself...is this it? Is this how I want my life? My answer was NO. 100% dissatisfaction will bring about a total change and I was a candidate ready for change. I was ready for more and I knew there was more to my life!

I made a commitment to the process of gratitude and spiritual development, which was the best decision I ever made. I learned God desired I live a life of abundance. I learned God had laid up blessings for me before the foundation of the world and gratitude was a key ingredient to me manifesting them into my life.

Here is what Gratitude released into my life:

1. Rain (blessings) from God during and after the drought.
2. Revelation and insight from God into various situations.
3. Way of escape out of unhealthy situations and circumstances.
4. Guidance on how to get myself out of tough places
5. Doorway to becoming a spiritual magnet
6. My promised harvest
7. God's Favor

As a result of the journey, I discovered my life's meaning and purpose. I am proud to tell you today I am confident, I have clarity, I have inner peace and I am more productive and focused than I've ever been. I celebrate my roles of mother, wife, success coach, leadership expert and entrepreneur. I am the CEO & Founder of Walk In Favor Life Coaching LLC, Living Authentically and Elevate Her, and I am grateful I get the opportunity to help women see the light at the end of the tunnel. My passion is seeing women become their beautiful authentic self and my contribution in making that happen is to help women who struggle with getting unstuck discover resilience so they own their brilliance and live their life free from fear guilt and apologies whether their Stuck is spiritual, personal or professional, I create unique action plans to help women get from where they are to where they want to be so they can experience happiness success and total fulfillment in life.

I want for you what I want for myself and this journal is a tool to assist you along the way. A few years ago, God trusted me with this assignment to help in the building of His Kingdom on Earth. He stated the purpose was to open up the eyes of His people to the daily benefits and blessings He bestows on us daily and that our recognition and gratefulness of His blessings would open the door for so much more in our lives.

If you're ready to begin seeing the desires of your heart walk into your life and live out your true purpose, take on the posture of gratitude, and this journal is designed to help you do just that. Thank You From A Grateful Heart is a guided journal that will help you capture God's Heart by focusing on His daily benefits in your life.

What is Gratitude

According to "Grace, Gratitude and the Glory of God" written by John Piper, gratitude is more than saying, "Thank you" when someone gives you something. Gratitude is more than an action that we decide to do by an act of will power. You can say the words, "thank you" when there is no gratitude in your heart at all. Custom may dictate that you say the words when you do not really appreciate what has been done for you. What it takes to turn the words, "thank you" into gratitude is the real genuine feeling of gratitude. Gratitude is a feeling that arises uncoerced in the heart. It cannot be willed into existence directly if it is not there.

Gratitude is a feeling not an act of will power. Moreover, it is a good feeling. When it rises in our hearts, we like it. It is part of happiness; it is a form of delight.

But gratitude is more than delighting in a gift. It is more than feeling happy that you got something you wanted. **Gratitude is a happy feeling you have about a giver because of his/her giving you something good or doing something good for you even if it is an <u>undeserved act of kindness.</u>**

When it comes to God, our righteousness is like filthy rage; therefore, we are not deserving of anything He does for us. His act of love and kindness isn't because we are so great... it is because He is so Great. It is God's desire for us to be grateful and remember what He has done for us. Psalms 103:1 says Bless the Lord, O my soul: and all that is within me, bless His Holy Name. Bless the Lord, O my soul, and forget NOT all his benefits! God doesn't have to be kind, God doesn't have to be nice; but since He is, the least we can do is say "Thank You".

Accessing the Power of Gratitude

The practice of gratitude as a tool for happiness has been in the mainstream for years. Long-term studies support gratitude's effectiveness, suggesting that a positive, appreciative attitude contributes to greater success in work, greater health, peak performance in sports and business, a higher sense of well-being, and a faster rate of recovery from surgery. "One of the greatest sins in our society is that of ingratitude. We err when we fail to give thanks to God for what He has done in our lives." Jack Wellman

While we may acknowledge the many benefits of gratitude, it still can be challenging to sustain. So many of us notice what is broken, undone or lacking in our lives. In order for gratitude to meet its full healing potential in our lives, it needs to become more than just a Thanksgiving word. We have to learn a new way of looking at things, a new habit, and that can take some time.

Gratitude is not a blindly optimistic approach in which the bad things in life are whitewashed or ignored. It is more a matter of where we put our focus and attention. Pain and injustice exist, but when we focus on the gifts of life, we gain a feeling of well-being. Gratitude balances us and gives us hope.

That is why *practicing* gratitude makes so much sense. When we practice giving thanks for all we have, instead of complaining about what we lack, we give ourselves the chance to see all of life as an opportunity and a blessing. **Being grateful allows us to see the bigger picture. Expressing thankfulness helps us remember that God is in total control.**

Some Ways to Practice Gratitude

Keep a gratitude journal in which you list things for which you are thankful. You can make daily lists using *"Thank You" from a Grateful Heart.* Greater frequency may be better for creating a new habit, but just keeping that journal where you can see it will remind you to think gratefully.
There are many things to be grateful for; what is on your list?

- ☑ Make a gratitude collage by drawing or pasting pictures.
- ☑ Practice gratitude around the dinner table or make it part of your nighttime routine.
- ☑ Make a game of finding the hidden blessing in a challenging situation.
- ☑ When you feel like complaining, make a gratitude list instead. Be amazed by how much better you feel.
- ☑ Notice how gratitude influences your life. Write about it, sing about it, and express thanks for gratitude.

As you practice the art of being grateful, an inner shift begins to occur, and you may be delighted to discover how content and hopeful you are feeling. That sense of fulfillment is gratitude at work!

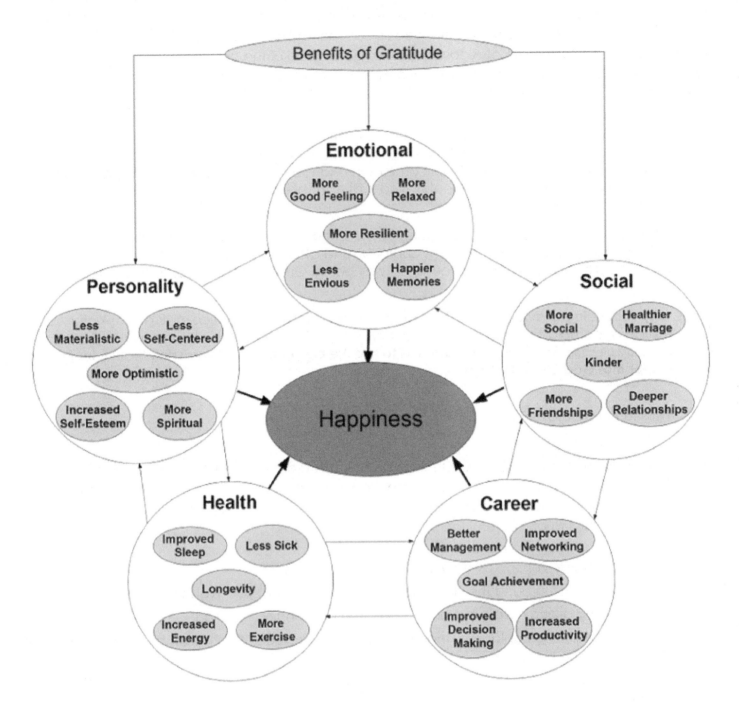

How to use Thank You From A Grateful Heart Journal

As you can see, creating the habit of writing in a Gratitude Journal has many benefits. Individuals who use gratitude journals reported increased enthusiasm, optimism, expectation, empowerment, passion, determination, and alertness. They were also more likely to help others and make progress towards their personal goals, compared to those who did not keep gratitude journals..

Although some recommend waiting until the end of the day to write down a few items you are grateful for, I suggest writing once in the morning and once in the evening. Writing in the morning allows you to seek and identify the blessings God has deposited into your life before your day overwhelms with the various task. Journaling during the morning puts you in the space of anticipating the great things God has planned for you on this day. Additionally, it allows you to establish a tone of thanksgiving for the rest of your day. Saturate your morning entries with items you are grateful for from the time you arise up to 12 noon.

Your evening entries will capture any additional blessings separate from your morning entries. You can also highlight specific or mind-blowing blessings that made a huge impact on your day. Writing in the evening permits you to end the day with a positive mindset and grander expectations for the next day.

Furthermore, use the evening to think about and list all the individuals who supported you during your day. Whether the person offered you encouraging words, prayers, well wishes, a helping hand, or any other act of kindness, be mindful of how God used them to assist you throughout your day. Do not forget to show them your appreciation and gratitude.

As you go about your day, remember to be intentional in detecting opportunities for gratitude. Psalm 68:19 informs us that God loads us daily with benefits; therefore, be on the lookout for them. This writing journey will cause you to become grateful for little; as a reward, you will notice you will find abundance.

Gratitude Journaling Tips
1. Be intentional about counting your blessings daily.
2. Jot down any blessings that arise as soon as possible.
3. If possible, include **"WHY"** you are grateful.
4. Write your entries from an angle that is appreciative, positive, enthusiastic, happy, hopeful and content.

Day 1

Dear God,

Thank You for sparing my life! Last year I had been feeling ill. Since it was around flu season, I passed it off as the simple flu, however, I just couldn't shake it this time. I started to find it difficult to breathe and sleep at night, and I decided to take a few days off work to nurse myself back to health. After about three days off work, I figured this was more than the flu because I had begun vomiting, and I could not hold down food. I went to an urgent care clinic, and they diagnosed me as having a respiratory infection, mind you, this was right before COVID-19 hit the US. I was prescribed antibiotics to try to fight the infection, but things seemed to start getting worse. The next day, my wife and I were laying on the couch and I could not inhale without having an intense pain in my chest. I could only breathe if I could take short, quick breaths. At this point, I mention to my wife that I needed to go to the hospital, and we made our way to the ER. After 5 hours in the waiting room, the doctors finally examined me. My initial lab results came back and the Doctor knew that they could not be right, so she had the nurses redo my labs. When the 2nd round of results came back, I could see the concern in her eyes. She came into the room, took a deep breath and said, "If these results are correct, you are currently in end-stage renal failure". My kidneys had completely shut down and according to the Doctors, they had no idea how I had made it to the ER. The said they needed to act fast as I was severely anemic and they didn't have time to get me to a room...I needed a blood transfusion right away. I remember holding my wife's hand and taking a moment to think, then telling the doctors that I would consent to a blood transfusion. My wife and the Doctor both looked at me and smiled and said we already did it, I had literally blanked out as my blood pressure had crashed. They told me that I was not out of the woods, as they moved me to the ICU for further treatment and emergency dialysis. I was eventually discharged and told that I would need dialysis for the rest of my life unless I received a kidney. I am truly grateful to God as 7 months later, I received a call from the hospital telling me they had a possible Kidney for me. This wasn't the first time that I had received that call, because I had received it a few times before and it always fell through. The next day, they called back and told me that Surgery was scheduled for me in about an hour and I had 30 minutes to get to the hospital. The transplant was a success, and I am truly grateful to God not just for the Kidney, but for showing me throughout the entire situation how important the gift of life was and how precious my loved ones are. Although the Kidney is truly a blessing, if I am honest, I looked at life differently as soon as I made it out of the ER well before the transplant.

Be thankful in all circumstances, for this is God's will for you who belong to Christ Jesus.
1 Thessalonians 5:18 NLT

Day 1 Morning

Check all of your existing blessings:

☐ *Health* ☐ *Shelter* ☐ *Food* ☐ *Clothing* ☐ *Family* ☐ *Life*

In addition to the above, today I am grateful for..

Be thankful in all circumstances, for this is God's will for you who belong to Christ Jesus.
1 Thessalonians 5:18 NLT

Day 1 Evening

As I close this day, I am truly Grateful for...

_____

_____

_____

_____

_____

_____

_____

_____

Write below anyone who blessed you with Kindness today.

_____   _____

_____   _____

_____   _____

How did you express to them your Gratitude?

_____

_____

_____

_____

Be thankful in all circumstances, for this is God's will for you who belong to Christ Jesus.
1 Thessalonians 5:18 NLT

Day 2

Dear God,

I am thankful for the simple things in life. My son has struggled academically for years and I am excited about our recent progress. Day after day I am blessed with an opportunity to watch my son work hard to complete his schoolwork independently, even when it's challenging. In the past he would be quick to give up and count himself out. I have prayed so many nights for him and I can see how you've been answering my prayer. Today was a huge win! My son started his homework without being instructed and he completed most of his assignments alone. I am so proud of him and thankful for his progress and faith to continue this unconventional way of learning. Thank you for being a God that never leaves me nor forsakes me.

And so, our God, we are giving you thanks, and we are praising your wonderful name!
1 Chronicles 29:13 ISV

Day 2 Morning

Check all of your existing blessings:

☐ *Health* ☐ *Shelter* ☐ *Food* ☐ *Clothing* ☐ *Family* ☐ *Life*

In addition to the above, today I am grateful for..

And so, our God, we are giving you thanks, and we are praising your wonderful name!
1 Chronicles 29:13 ISV

Day 2 Evening

As I close this day, I am truly Grateful for...

Write below anyone who blessed you with Kindness today.

------------------------------------   ------------------------------------

------------------------------------   ------------------------------------

------------------------------------   ------------------------------------

How did you express to them your Gratitude?

And so, our God, we are giving you thanks, and we are praising your wonderful name!
1 Chronicles 29:13 ISV

Day 3

Dear God,
I am excited for another reason to be grateful for today. My daughter went to the hospital due to extreme pain. The doctors found that she had a mass near her ovaries. Due to her abdomen filled with blood, they had to perform emergency surgery to remove it.

I am thankful that You, the Great Physician, intercepted the plan of the enemy. She successfully made it out of surgery and is now recovering. Father, I give You all the glory for Your protection over my loved ones and me.

Give thanks to the LORD, for he is good; his love endures forever.
Psalm 107:1 NIV

Day 3 Morning

☐ *Health* ☐ *Shelter* ☐ *Food* ☐ *Clothing* ☐ *Family* ☐ *Life*

In addition to the above, today I am grateful for...

\---

\---

\---

\---

\---

\---

\---

\---

\---

\---

\---

\---

\---

\---

\---

Give thanks to the LORD, for he is good; his love endures forever.
Psalm 107:1 NIV

Day 3 Evening

As I close this day, I am truly Grateful for...

Write below anyone who blessed you with Kindness today.

-------------------------------------   -------------------------------------

-------------------------------------   -------------------------------------

-------------------------------------   -------------------------------------

How did you express to them your Gratitude?

Give thanks to the LORD, for he is good; his love endures forever.
Psalm 107:1 NIV

Day 4

Dear God,

I want to start by saying thanks for being you and having more excellent ways and methods than we do. You love me even when I am unlovable, and that blows my mind how unconditional your love is. Today I want to thank you for revelation and manifestation. Because my husband doesn't have a relationship with you, it has been the basis of much discontentment. I have found myself nagging and trying to force him into faith. After a lot of disappointment, I realized that method wasn't working. I was taught, when you've tried everything else and nothing works, prayer will do it. I decided to shift from nagging to praying.

Yesterday my husband came home and told me he believes You are working on him. Talk about stunned! Talk about stunned! This is so amazing for me because You said our prayers would avail much, and they did just that. Today I thank you for showing me that my conduct and not my words will win him to you, and I thank you for the revelations you are giving him. Thank you for helping me realize the error of my ways and showing me how to begin working on my flaws rather than pointing the blame at him and others around me.

I thank you for answering my prayer and giving me victory!
Psalm 118:21 NLT

Day 4 Morning

Check all of your existing blessings:

☐ *Health* ☐ *Shelter* ☐ *Food* ☐ *Clothing* ☐ *Family* ☐ *Life*

In addition to the above, today I am grateful for...

I thank you for answering my prayer and giving me victory!
Psalm 118:21 NLT

Day 4 Evening

As I close this day, I am truly Grateful for...

Write below anyone who blessed you with Kindness today.

--------------------------------------   --------------------------------------
--------------------------------------   --------------------------------------
--------------------------------------   --------------------------------------

How did you express to them your Gratitude?

I thank you for answering my prayer and giving me victory!
Psalm 118:21 NLT

Day 5

Dear God,
Today I am grateful for my knowledge of you. Your grace and mercy renew me every day. I have a sound mind, I'm in good health, and I'm satisfied. Thank you for all the things you have done for me and the things that I thought I needed that you kept away from me. Thank you for always being the same yesterday, today, and forever.

Give thanks unto the LORD, call upon his name, make known his deeds among the people.
1 Chronicles 16:8 KJV

Day 5 Morning

Check all of your existing blessings:

☐ Health ☐ Shelter ☐ Food ☐ Clothing ☐ Family ☐ Life

In addition to the above, today I am grateful for...

Give thanks unto the LORD, call upon his name, make known his deeds among the people.
1 Chronicles 16:8 KJV

Day 5 Evening

As I close this day, I am truly Grateful for…………………………………………………

Write below anyone who blessed you with Kindness today.

---------------------------------   ----------------------------------

---------------------------------   ----------------------------------

---------------------------------   ----------------------------------

How did you express to them your Gratitude?

Give thanks unto the LORD, call upon his name, make known his deeds among the people.
1 Chronicles 16:8 KJV

Day 6

Dear God,

Today I am thanking you for traveling grace and mercies. I also want to thank you for such a great support system of friends and family. Often, I felt that something was lacking because I didn't have an extensive support system, but today I thank you for bringing me the quality of people versus a significant number of people. Thank you for beginning to renew my mind and circumcise my heart. I pray that you continue the work you have begun in me for my good and your glory. I thank you in advance because I know the answers to my prayers are yes and Amen..

And give thanks for everything to God the Father in the name of our Lord Jesus Christ.
Ephesians 5:20 NLT

Day 6 Morning

Check all of your existing blessings:

☐ Health ☐ Shelter ☐ Food ☐ Clothing ☐ Family ☐ Life

In addition to the above, today I am grateful for...

And give thanks for everything to God the Father in the name of our Lord Jesus Christ.
Ephesians 5:20 NLT

Day 6 Evening

As I close this day, I am truly Grateful for...

Write below anyone who blessed you with Kindness today.

------------------------------------   ------------------------------------

------------------------------------   ------------------------------------

------------------------------------   ------------------------------------

How did you express to them your Gratitude?

And give thanks for everything to God the Father in the name of our Lord Jesus Christ.
Ephesians 5:20 NLT

Day 7

Father in The name of Jesus!

I am so grateful. My son has been praying for a personal basketball trainer and coach. He desires to increase his skill set as well as his basketball I.Q. Today you put me in the presence of a young athletic coach that is a perfect match for him. My son's prayer has been answered. The best part of this newfound relationship is the coach attended Christian Educational institutions ALL OF HIS LIFE! He's a believer in You, Lord. You are the only one with the power to open doors like this! Thank you, God, for you answered the prayer of a little 14-year-old child. His heart is grateful, and so is mine.

Thank you, Jesus!

Let all that I am praise the LORD; may I never forget the good things he does for me.

Psalm 103:2 NLT

Day 7 Morning

Check all of your existing blessings:

☐ Health ☐ Shelter ☐ Food ☐ Clothing ☐ Family ☐ Life

In addition to the above, today I am grateful for...

Let all that I am praise the LORD; may I never forget the good things he does for me.
Psalm 103:2 NLT

Day 7 Evening

As I close this day, I am truly Grateful for...

Write below anyone who blessed you with Kindness today.

--   --

--   --

--   --

How did you express to them your Gratitude?

Let all that I am praise the LORD; may I never forget the good things he does for me.
Psalm 103:2 NLT

Day 8

Father in Heaven,
Thank you for being a good, good Father. I am forever grateful for your love and attention you give to me.

On October 21st, you accompanied me to surgery. After the surgery, I was doing good; however, my hemoglobin dropped from 12 to 7.1. As a result, I passed out, and my blood pressure was super low. Immediately I was given two units of blood, which stabilized me. Shortly after the blood transfusion, I received a phone call from my son telling me my dad passed away. Father, it was so hard, but Your Grace kept me, and You're the reason I am here today sharing my testimony. I want to tell the world You Father have indeed been good to me! Praise Your Holy name.

Thank God for this gift too wonderful for words!
2 Corinthians 9:15 NLT

Day 8 Morning

Check all of your existing blessings:

☐ *Health*   ☐ *Shelter*   ☐ *Food*   ☐ *Clothing*   ☐ *Family*   ☐ *Life*

In addition to the above, today I am grateful for...

Thank God for this gift too wonderful for words!
2 Corinthians 9:15 NLT

Day 8 Evening

As I close this day, I am truly Grateful for...

Write below anyone who blessed you with Kindness today.

------------------------------------   ------------------------------------

------------------------------------   ------------------------------------

------------------------------------   ------------------------------------

How did you express to them your Gratitude?

Thank God for this gift too wonderful for words!
2 Corinthians 9:15 NLT

Day 9

Lord,
I love you, and I thank you today for giving me the ability to provide for my family. You never fail to keep your promises. You said if I honor you with my tithe, you will meet all my needs. I honored you by stepping into the supernatural flow of sowing and reaping, and I must say you moved me from lack into abundance. My mindset about giving has changed completely. I used to think I couldn't afford to give; now I know I can't afford to give. You are an awesome wonder, and I praise you for your faithfulness to my family and me. Thank you for the confidence in knowing that when I seek you, you will be there. Thank you forever! In Jesus name Amen.

I will give thanks to the LORD with all my heart, I will declare all your wonderful deeds.
Psalm 9:1 ISV

Day 9 Morning

Check all of your existing blessings:

☐ Health ☐ Shelter ☐ Food ☐ Clothing ☐ Family ☐ Life

In addition to the above, today I am grateful for...

I will give thanks to the LORD with all my heart, I will declare all your wonderful deeds.
Psalm 9:1 ISV

Day 9 Evening

As I close this day, I am truly Grateful for...

Write below anyone who blessed you with Kindness today.

-----------------------------------   -----------------------------------

-----------------------------------   -----------------------------------

-----------------------------------   -----------------------------------

How did you express to them your Gratitude?

I will give thanks to the LORD with all my heart, I will declare all your wonderful deeds.
Psalm 9:1 ISV

Day 10

Lord,

Today I thank you for reconnecting me with my dear friend. Only you know the trials and tribulations she has undergone throughout this year, but I come to you now for not allowing her to fall from your care. You said you wouldn't lose any of us, and you have honored your word in her life. Lord, please continue to strengthen her on her journey. I thank you in advance for the ministry you are developing in her. Thank you for giving her the courage to share her story and triumph. Her journey has blessed my life.

Rejoice in the LORD, O you righteous, and give thanks to his holy name!
Psalm 97:12 ESV

Day 10 Morning

Check all of your existing blessings:

☐ *Health* ☐ *Shelter* ☐ *Food* ☐ *Clothing* ☐ *Family* ☐ *Life*

In addition to the above, today I am grateful for...

Rejoice in the LORD, O you righteous, and give thanks to his holy name!
Psalm 97:12 ESV

Day 10 Evening

As I close this day, I am truly Grateful for..

Write below anyone who blessed you with Kindness today.

--   --

--   --

--   --

How did you express to them your Gratitude?

Rejoice in the LORD, O you righteous, and give thanks to his holy name!
Psalm 97:12 ESV

Day 11

Lord from the depths of my heart,
Thank you for elevating my daughter's confidence despite the mean things that have been said and done to her in the past. Peer pressure and bullying have been a problem, and sometimes it has become overwhelming. Because of your favor, she cheers with remarkable confidence and a gorgeous smile.

 Thank you for inviting her to pray to you, thank you for building her faith in such a way that she WAITS for you! You are a giving Father, always thinking of us. Help us to all be more like you. Tonight, I offer to you a million thank you's and a trillion kisses. I love you! In Jesus name Amen.

God, we thank you; we thank you because you are near. We tell about the miracles you do.

Psalm 75:1 NCV

Day 11 Morning

Check all of your existing blessings:

☐ Health ☐ Shelter ☐ Food ☐ Clothing ☐ Family ☐ Life

In addition to the above, today I am grateful for……………………………………

God, we thank you; we thank you because you are near. We tell about the miracles you do.
Psalm 75:1 NCV

Day 11 Evening

As I close this day, I am truly Grateful for...

Write below anyone who blessed you with Kindness today.

-----------------------------------   -----------------------------------

-----------------------------------   -----------------------------------

-----------------------------------   -----------------------------------

How did you express to them your Gratitude?

God, we thank you; we thank you because you are near. We tell about the miracles you do.

Psalm 75:1 NCV

Day 12

Lord, I want to thank you for sending someone my way to speak healing in my life when I deeply needed healing. I am grateful for the ability to stop and notice your Holy Spirit flowing through a young man who was listening as I described the pain I was experiencing daily in my knees over the past year. Upon finishing my statement, this rugged look was on his face, which made me stop and pay attention. He then said, "Ms. Kim you don't believe you're healed, but Ms. Kim you are healed in the name of Jesus"! It was right at that moment God's healing power flowed through me. I was reminded of the power that the young man was exercising and the power that I have in Jesus name. Sometimes it is in our words as well as in our belief that we block our blessings. We can't just merely speak it; we have to believe it and walk in it. I realized I needed to activate the belief that

already existed within me. Since that day in June, I have walked in my healing and I say daily, "I am healed in the name of Jesus", with an unwavering doubt. I continuously recall to my mind the words of Ephesians 3: 20, Now to him who is able to do exceedingly abundantly above all that we ask or think, according to the power that works in us. There are so many accounts in my life where you have been so faithful to me, God and continuously showing me favor. I lift my hands in total praise to you.

O give thanks to the LORD, for He is good; For His loving kindness is everlasting.
1 Chronicles 16:34 ESV

Day 12 Morning

Check all of your existing blessings:

☐ *Health* ☐ *Shelter* ☐ *Food* ☐ *Clothing* ☐ *Family* ☐ *Life*

In addition to the above, today I am grateful for……………………………………………

O give thanks to the LORD, for He is good; For His loving kindness is everlasting.
1 Chronicles 16:34 ESV

Day 12 Evening

As I close this day, I am truly Grateful for..

Write below anyone who blessed you with Kindness today.

------------------------------------   ------------------------------------

------------------------------------   ------------------------------------

------------------------------------   ------------------------------------

How did you express to them your Gratitude?

O give thanks to the LORD, for He is good; For His loving kindness is everlasting.
1 Chronicles 16:34 ESV

Day 13

Dear Lord,
I'm thankful for my lovely wife. She's beautiful, caring and PERFECT for me and our children.

It is good to give thanks to the LORD and to sing praise to your name, Most High;

Psalm 92:1 KJV

Day 13 Morning

Check all of your existing blessings:

☐ Health   ☐ Shelter   ☐ Food   ☐ Clothing   ☐ Family   ☐ Life

In addition to the above, today I am grateful for...

It is good to give thanks to the LORD and to sing praise to your name, Most High;

Psalm 92:1 KJV

Day 13 Evening

As I close this day, I am truly Grateful for..

_____

_____

_____

_____

_____

_____

_____

_____

_____

Write below anyone who blessed you with Kindness today.

_____   _____

_____   _____

_____   _____

How did you express to them your Gratitude?

_____

_____

_____

_____

_____

It is good to give thanks to the LORD and to sing praise to your name, Most High;

Psalm 92:1 KJV

Day 14

Dear God,

Today I am grateful for learning how to enjoy the process. Instead of getting discouraged during the wait, I am learning to embrace these moments because they set the foundation for my future. No longer will I poison my promises by speaking negatively about them when it doesn't seem like it's working out the way I hoped. I am learning to trust in you and trust that what was mean for evil you use for good. I am grateful for the insight you are providing me and the way you are revealing me to myself as weird as that sounds. I am learning who I am all the good and bad things about me and I'm on a journey to change in order to look more like you. So, thank you for the knowledge and willingness to face myself, my flaws, and my responsibility in every area of my life. This process is preparing me for the next phase in my life and for that I thank you.

This is the day the LORD has made. Let's rejoice and be glad today!
Psalm 118:24 GWT

Day 14 Morning

Check all of your existing blessings:

☐ Health ☐ Shelter ☐ Food ☐ Clothing ☐ Family ☐ Life

In addition to the above, today I am grateful for...

This is the day the LORD has made. Let's rejoice and be glad today!
Psalm 118:24 GWT

Day 14 Evening

As I close this day, I am truly Grateful for...

Write below anyone who blessed you with Kindness today.

------------------------------------   ------------------------------------
------------------------------------   ------------------------------------
------------------------------------   ------------------------------------

How did you express to them your Gratitude?

This is the day the LORD has made. Let's rejoice and be glad today!
Psalm 118:24 GWT

Day 15

Thank you Abba Father for healing and deliverance!

January, I was diagnosed with beginning cataracts. By February the cataract had progressively gotten worse and was immediately scheduled for surgery. Due to the pandemic my eye surgery were postponed until June and July of 2020. After wearing glasses for over fifty years. Also being told that I would loss sight in my left eye, because of a children accident. God has restored my vision.
One more thing during my first surgery I could hear someone singing" God has smiled on me, what was amazing is after a while I realized it was me Praising My Lord and Savior all while I was going through.

Give thanks to the Lord because he is good. His love continues forever.
Psalm 136:1 NCV

Day 15 Morning

Check all of your existing blessings:

☐ Health ☐ Shelter ☐ Food ☐ Clothing ☐ Family ☐ Life

In addition to the above, today I am grateful for...

Give thanks to the Lord because he is good. His love continues forever.
Psalm 136:1 NCV

Day 15 Evening

As I close this day, I am truly Grateful for..

Write below anyone who blessed you with Kindness today.

-------------------------------------   -------------------------------------
-------------------------------------   -------------------------------------
-------------------------------------   -------------------------------------

How did you express to them your Gratitude?

Give thanks to the Lord because he is good. His love continues forever.
Psalm 136:1 NCV

Day 16

Father,

Today I thank you as I hear the voices of my children laughing and talking. I thank you for giving them to me. You have blessed me with children in many different ways. I've given natural birth to four, but I am "mommy" to seven! (Did you send me to a foreign land to bring home TWO babies??) Only you can do what you have done in our lives: only you, God. You didn't have to do it, but you did. You chose me, and I will serve you all the days of my life!

Give thanks to the Lord and pray to him. Tell the nations what he has done.
Psalm 105:1 NCV

Day 16 Morning

Check all of your existing blessings:

☐ Health ☐ Shelter ☐ Food ☐ Clothing ☐ Family ☐ Life

In addition to the above, today I am grateful for...

Give thanks to the Lord and pray to him. Tell the nations what he has done.
Psalm 105:1 NCV

Day 16 Evening

As I close this day, I am truly Grateful for...

Write below anyone who blessed you with Kindness today.

--------------------------------------   --------------------------------------
--------------------------------------   --------------------------------------
--------------------------------------   --------------------------------------

How did you express to them your Gratitude?

Give thanks to the Lord and pray to him. Tell the nations what he has done.
Psalm 105:1 NCV

Day 17

To my Heavenly Father:

As I look back on my two-year journey, I am once again in awe. Two years ago, I prayed to be "loosed" and freed to take a tremendous leap and change my entire life. Fast forward, by the end of the first year, I ended up in a new city and a wheelchair, more ill than I had ever been. However, I pressed on, Father, trusting you on the journey. Thank you, Father, that now, today, at the end of year two, I am in my dream home on ACRES of land. I'm a published author, and all of my needs are met beyond my wildest dreams! As Paul said, these were just temporary afflictions. You are so faithful, and I thank you, Jesus.

Make thankfulness your sacrifice to God, and keep the vows you made to the Most High.

Psalm 50:14 NLT

Day 17 Morning

Check all of your existing blessings:

☐ Health ☐ Shelter ☐ Food ☐ Clothing ☐ Family ☐ Life

In addition to the above, today I am grateful for...

Make thankfulness your sacrifice to God, and keep the vows you made to the Most High.
Psalm 50:14 NLT

Day 17 Evening

As I close this day, I am truly Grateful for...

Write below anyone who blessed you with Kindness today.

-----------------------------------   -----------------------------------

-----------------------------------   -----------------------------------

-----------------------------------   -----------------------------------

How did you express to them your Gratitude?

Make thankfulness your sacrifice to God, and keep the vows you made to the Most High.
Psalm 50:14 NLT

Day 18

Father in Heaven,

For the past 2 years, I've been praying for financial assistance to pay off my student loan. Because I am a tither, I've been asking you to open up the windows of Heaven and pour out a financial blessing. Today, I thank you for the light at the end of the tunnel. Today, I had an extensive and informative conversation with a representative from my student loan company. At the end of the exchange I was blessed with the option of having my entire student loan forgiven. Lord that is a $47,000 debt forgiveness. Lord, I recognize it was only you who opened this door of favor. I am forever grateful!

My heart rejoices, and I give thanks to him with my song.
Psalm 28:7 KJV

Day 18 Morning

Check all of your existing blessings:

☐ *Health* ☐ *Shelter* ☐ *Food* ☐ *Clothing* ☐ *Family* ☐ *Life*

In addition to the above, today I am grateful for...

My heart rejoices, and I give thanks to him with my song.
Psalm 28:7 KJV

Day 18 Evening

As I close this day, I am truly Grateful for...

Write below anyone who blessed you with Kindness today.

------------------------------------   ------------------------------------
------------------------------------   ------------------------------------
------------------------------------   ------------------------------------

How did you express to them your Gratitude?

My heart rejoices, and I give thanks to him with my song.
Psalm 28:7 KJV

Day 19

Dear Heavenly Father,

You have been so gracious and so good to my family. I find that I often have prayed for abundance and prosperity to flow towards my children. Lord your word says we are to ask anything in your name and it will be given. Today, I celebrate the confirmation of my prayer. In one-week Father, you gave one of my children two bonuses totaling $1200 along with a $5 hourly increase. The best part is he wasn't expecting either of these blessings! So I thank you Father for being so gracious and so rewarding! You are a good God. I love you more than anything.

I will thank the LORD because he is just
Psalm 7:17 NLT

Day 19 Morning

Check all of your existing blessings:

☐ Health ☐ Shelter ☐ Food ☐ Clothing ☐ Family ☐ Life

In addition to the above, today I am grateful for...

I will thank the LORD because he is just
Psalm 7:17 NLT

Day 19 Evening

As I close this day, I am truly Grateful for...

Write below anyone who blessed you with Kindness today.

--   --
--   --
--   --

How did you express to them your Gratitude?

I will thank the LORD because he is just
Psalm 7:17 NLT

Day 20

Father,

Thank you for answering my fervent prayers! Money came just in time! Unexpected but certainly needed and deeply appreciated. Honestly God, who has people just walking up to them handing them money? My husband does, one of your faithful and hard-working servants. Lord, when you put our family on the heart and mind of others, it's a very sweet and warm feeling that can't be explained. Thank you for the obedience of those who answered your request to bless me and my family. You are a good and awesome Father and I'm so grateful for your unfailing and unwavering love. In Jesus name, Amen.

Always be thankful.
Colossians 3:15 NCV

Day 20 Morning

Check all of your existing blessings:

☐ Health ☐ Shelter ☐ Food ☐ Clothing ☐ Family ☐ Life

In addition to the above, today I am grateful for...

Always be thankful.
Colossians 3:15 NCV

Day 20 Evening

As I close this day, I am truly Grateful for...

_____

_____

_____

_____

_____

_____

_____

_____

_____

_____

Write below anyone who blessed you with Kindness today.

_____   _____

_____   _____

_____   _____

How did you express to them your Gratitude?

_____

_____

_____

_____

_____

_____

Always be thankful.
Colossians 3:15 NCV

Day 21

Thank you Lord for hearing my humble cry! My knee had been aching terribly for days. I prayed over it. I even put healing oil on it. Yet, it was still hurting. Then, you showed me why it was hurting. I made the adjustment, and the pain has not been back! I love the way you take care of me! In Jesus name, Amen.

Forever Grateful

Enter his gates with thanksgiving, and his courts with praise! Give thanks to him; bless his name!

Psalm 100:4 ESV

Day 21 Morning

Check all of your existing blessings:

☐ Health ☐ Shelter ☐ Food ☐ Clothing ☐ Family ☐ Life

In addition to the above, today I am grateful for...

Enter his gates with thanksgiving, and his courts with praise! Give thanks to him; bless his name!
Psalm 100:4 ESV

Day 21 Evening

As I close this day, I am truly Grateful for...

_____

_____

_____

_____

_____

_____

_____

_____

_____

Write below anyone who blessed you with Kindness today.

_____   _____

_____   _____

_____   _____

How did you express to them your Gratitude?

_____

_____

_____

_____

_____

_____

Enter his gates with thanksgiving, and his courts with praise! Give thanks to him; bless his name!
Psalm 100:4 ESV

Day 22

Jehovah God,

Only You know my inner thoughts! Only you know what I went to bed with last night. Only You know how I carried it into worship today. Only You had the ability to take it away. Thank you for my Bishop! He's a true Man of God who stays on his face before you seeking instruction before he brings the Word of God to the flock. Thank you that the word was definitely for me today.

Cast your cares, Favor in coming my way, but favor can't work with a bad attitude! You said not to give up, the race will be given to me because I endure until the end. Thank you for encouraging my soul and making me whole again. I have given you every care and I wait trusting that you will give me instruction and guidance. Thank you for your concern in every aspect of my life. I truly love you! In Jesus name, Amen.

Praise the LORD, all you nations. Praise him, all you people of the earth.
Psalm 117:1 NLT

Day 22 Morning

Check all of your existing blessings:

☐ Health ☐ Shelter ☐ Food ☐ Clothing ☐ Family ☐ Life

In addition to the above, today I am grateful for...

Praise the LORD, all you nations. Praise him, all you people of the earth.
Psalm 117:1 NLT

Day 22 Evening

As I close this day, I am truly Grateful for...

_____

_____

_____

_____

_____

_____

_____

_____

_____

Write below anyone who blessed you with Kindness today.

_____   _____

_____   _____

_____   _____

How did you express to them your Gratitude?

_____

_____

_____

_____

_____

Praise the LORD, all you nations. Praise him, all you people of the earth.
Psalm 117:1 NLT

Day 23

Thank You, God for your favor today. You kicked down a door that only you could open for me. I so appreciate that you loved me enough to bless me with national business exposure for my new business. I am new to business, yet I was approached with an opportunity to launch a national radio talk show. You're the only one who can make things happen that quickly and that effortlessly. You nudged me to get the information. You reminded me to apply. You made it affordable to where the decision was a no brainer! Thank You for smiling down on me today. I'm excited and will honor the opportunity you have given me.

Bless our God, O peoples; let the sound of his praise be heard
Psalm 66:8 ESV

Day 23 Morning

Check all of your existing blessings:

☐ Health ☐ Shelter ☐ Food ☐ Clothing ☐ Family ☐ Life

In addition to the above, today I am grateful for..

Bless our God, O peoples; let the sound of his praise be heard
Psalm 66:8 ESV

Day 23 Evening

As I close this day, I am truly Grateful for..

Write below anyone who blessed you with Kindness today.

-------------------------------------   -------------------------------------
-------------------------------------   -------------------------------------
-------------------------------------   -------------------------------------

How did you express to them your Gratitude?

Bless our God, O peoples; let the sound of his praise be heard
Psalm 66:8 ESV

Day 24

Thank You, God for my grandmother. While I am missing her today on her birthday, my heart is warmed by the memories of our times of talking and praying and cooking and sharing. You gave me the best grandmother a woman could have. You allowed me to see a woman of God who always turned to her faith to make it through each and every day. Today, I follow that model because I want to be the one my son sees turning to my faith to make it through each day so he will follow the lead that Grandma did for me.

You are my God and I will give you thanks! You are my God and I will praise you!
Psalm 118:28 NET Bible

Day 24 Morning

Check all of your existing blessings:

☐ Health ☐ Shelter ☐ Food ☐ Clothing ☐ Family ☐ Life

In addition to the above, today I am grateful for...

You are my God and I will give you thanks! You are my God and I will praise you!
Psalm 118:28 NET Bible

Day 24 Evening

As I close this day, I am truly Grateful for...

Write below anyone who blessed you with Kindness today.

--   --
--   --
--   --

How did you express to them your Gratitude?

You are my God and I will give you thanks! You are my God and I will praise you!
Psalm 118:28 NET Bible

Day 25

Thank You, God for true friendship. Thank you for the ear of a friend who didn't have to listen to my challenges but she did. Thank you for speaking a word to her to share with me that took all of the pain and inner hurt away. Thank you for allowing me to see the reason for a major disappointment and for allowing me to move past the pain and toward healing. Thank you for the peace that passes all understanding and for allowing me to begin to heal my heart.

Bless the LORD, O my soul! O LORD my God, you are very great! You are clothed with splendor and majesty
Psalms 104:1 ESV

Day 25 Morning

Check all of your existing blessings:

☐ Health ☐ Shelter ☐ Food ☐ Clothing ☐ Family ☐ Life

In addition to the above, today I am grateful for...

_____

_____

_____

_____

_____

_____

_____

_____

_____

_____

_____

_____

_____

_____

_____

_____

_____

Bless the LORD, O my soul! O LORD my God, you are very great! You are clothed with splendor and majesty

Psalms 104:1 ESV

Day 25 Evening

As I close this day, I am truly Grateful for...

Write below anyone who blessed you with Kindness today.

-------------------------------------   -------------------------------------
-------------------------------------   -------------------------------------
-------------------------------------   -------------------------------------

How did you express to them your Gratitude?

Bless the LORD, O my soul! O LORD my God, you are very great! You are clothed with splendor and majesty
Psalms 104:1 ESV

Day 26

I thank God for His Provision. He is my Jehovah About 4 years ago I was diagnosed with M.S . ... INSTANTLY I was paralyzed from the neck down, I was 80 LBS. my feet were red & raw. My body was sore & weak. I felt like giving up at that time. I had to have physical therapy for a few years . In the mist of this I was hospitalized several times due to my feet being red , raw & feeling like I was being ELECTROCUTED !!! During one of those hospitalizations I was left in the care of a 20 something nurse who was CLEARLY INEXPERIENCED because I was giving WAY TOO MUCH MEDICATION (MORPHINE TO BE EXACT) & winding up falling into a MEDICALLY INDUCED COMA !!!! During this journey I felt like I was just sleep in a dream .... in the "dream " I was walking down a VERY DARK TUNNEL .. During my walk through this dream I kept hearing someone calling my name "Deanna , Deanna , Deanna !!!! The voice began to ANOY me so I kept waking away from the voice UNTIL A VERY LARGE HAND GENTLY PUSHED BACK TO THAT ANNOYING VOICE AGAIN... & I FINALLY WOKE UP ... To HUNDREDS OF DRS SURROUNDING ME asking me if I was ok!!! The ONLY THING that I could think to say is was MY GOD.

I remember what the Lord did; I remember the miracles you did long ago.
Psalm 77:11 NCV

Day 26 Morning

Check all of your existing blessings:

☐ Health ☐ Shelter ☐ Food ☐ Clothing ☐ Family ☐ Life

In addition to the above, today I am grateful for...

I remember what the Lord did; I remember the miracles you did long ago.
Psalm 77:11 NCV

Day 26 Evening

As I close this day, I am truly Grateful for...

Write below anyone who blessed you with Kindness today.

--   --
--   --
--   --

How did you express to them your Gratitude?

I remember what the Lord did; I remember the miracles you did long ago.
Psalm 77:11 NCV

Day 27

My God is Awesome! Almost 19 years ago, my family and I lost everything. We had nothing but the clothes on our backs and we had to live in my dad's basement due to that and other unforeseen circumstances. The rebuilding process wasn't easy but it was worth it. Today, I am happy to say that GOD has BLESSED us with more than we could ever imagine. He is truly AMAZING!

I will praise God's name in song and glorify him with thanksgiving.
Psalm 69:30 NIV

Day 27 Morning

Check all of your existing blessings:

☐ Health ☐ Shelter ☐ Food ☐ Clothing ☐ Family ☐ Life

In addition to the above, today I am grateful for………………………………………

I will praise God's name in song and glorify him with thanksgiving.
Psalm 69:30 NIV

Day 27 Evening

As I close this day, I am truly Grateful for...

_____

_____

_____

_____

_____

_____

_____

_____

_____

Write below anyone who blessed you with Kindness today.

_____   _____

_____   _____

_____   _____

How did you express to them your Gratitude?

_____

_____

_____

_____

_____

_____

I will praise God's name in song and glorify him with thanksgiving.
Psalm 69:30 NIV

Day 28

Thank You, God for my son. My mini me is the thing I love the most after You. You have blessed me with an amazing little person who amazes me on a daily basis. Thank You for giving him such an un-limited mind and a heart for You. Thank You for his kindness, his silliness and his desire to be the best man he can be. When I am filling down, I am able to glance and my mini me and release there are many reasons for me to rejoice. Thank You for blessing me with because he is definitely the best part of me.

But I will praise and thank you while I give sacrifices to you
Jonah 2:9 NCV

Day 28 Morning

Check all of your existing blessings:

☐ Health ☐ Shelter ☐ Food ☐ Clothing ☐ Family ☐ Life

In addition to the above, today I am grateful for...

But I will praise and thank you while I give sacrifices to you
Jonah 2:9 NCV

Day 28 Evening

As I close this day, I am truly Grateful for...

Write below anyone who blessed you with Kindness today.

-----------------------------------   -----------------------------------
-----------------------------------   -----------------------------------
-----------------------------------   -----------------------------------

How did you express to them your Gratitude?

But I will praise and thank you while I give sacrifices to you
Jonah 2:9 NCV

Day 29

Thank You, God for an amazing word through my Pastor today. Thank You for the word on diligence and on staying ready for a fight from the enemy. There have been attacks in my personal and professional life. It has been devastating and the more I complained the worse it got. I decided to read your word and seek out the promises you made for my future. Thank You for allowing me to peak into my future through faith and see in the spirit what I have yet to see in the natural. I know that you have a plan to prosper me. Thank You for sharing with me that being a Christian isn't a 9-5 job and that sometimes you have to take the fight to the enemy to get where God is taking you. Father, thank you for teaching me how to submit to you, resist the devil and cause him to flee in Jesus name Amen.

But we thank God! He gives us the victory through our Lord Jesus Christ.
1 Corinthians 15:57 NCV

Day 29 Morning

Check all of your existing blessings:

☐ Health ☐ Shelter ☐ Food ☐ Clothing ☐ Family ☐ Life

In addition to the above, today I am grateful for...

But we thank God! He gives us the victory through our Lord Jesus Christ.
1 Corinthians 15:57 NCV

Day 29 Evening

As I close this day, I am truly Grateful for...

Write below anyone who blessed you with Kindness today.

-----------------------------------   -----------------------------------
-----------------------------------   -----------------------------------
-----------------------------------   -----------------------------------

How did you express to them your Gratitude?

But we thank God! He gives us the victory through our Lord Jesus Christ.
1 Corinthians 15:57 NCV

Day 30

Thank You, God for my career. You opened a door that I didn't even see and ushered me into a place where I am appreciated and nurtured. Thank You for a great team that surrounds me. They make me laugh and help me every step of the way as I am still learning a brand new field. Thank You for my customers who are accepting me as their new account manager and open to my ideas for their success. Thank You for a company that gives me the opportunity to earn a great living, provide excellent benefits and opportunities for advancement. Thank You for the job that came and found me. I'm excited and work as unto You and not man each day.

Let us come to him with thanksgiving. Let us sing psalms of praise to him.
Psalm 95:2 NLT

Day 30 Morning

Check all of your existing blessings:

☐ *Health* ☐ *Shelter* ☐ *Food* ☐ *Clothing* ☐ *Family* ☐ *Life*

In addition to the above, today I am grateful for...

Let us come to him with thanksgiving. Let us sing psalms of praise to him.
Psalm 95:2 NL

Day 30 Evening

As I close this day, I am truly Grateful for...

Write below anyone who blessed you with Kindness today.

--------------------------------------   --------------------------------------
--------------------------------------   --------------------------------------
--------------------------------------   --------------------------------------

How did you express to them your Gratitude?

Let us come to him with thanksgiving. Let us sing psalms of praise to him.
Psalm 95:2 NLT

Day 31

Thank You for a caring father for my son. While things didn't work out for our marriage, he continues to set the standard that my son sees as a man of God. I'm thankful that we are friends and that we parent our son with the same goals in mind. Thank You for always allowing peace between us and for our focus to be united to make sure our son grows into all that You have called him to be.

Thank the LORD! Praise his name! Tell the nations what he has done.
Isaiah 12:4 NLT

Day 31 Morning

Check all of your existing blessings:

☐ Health ☐ Shelter ☐ Food ☐ Clothing ☐ Family ☐ Life

In addition to the above, today I am grateful for………………………………………

Thank the LORD! Praise his name! Tell the nations what he has done.
Isaiah 12:4 NLT

Day 31 Evening

As I close this day, I am truly Grateful for..

Write below anyone who blessed you with Kindness today.

--   --

--   --

--   --

How did you express to them your Gratitude?

Thank the LORD! Praise his name! Tell the nations what he has done.
Isaiah 12:4 NLT

Day 32

Thank You, God for fellowship. I'm grateful to be at a house of worship where the leadership can come together to laugh, share stories and support each other in this thing called life. Thank you for 'real' people who keep it '100' but still honor God with the works of their hands and their hearts. I have seen many people "play church" however, this is not that type of congregation. They do more than lip service, they put action behind their faith. Thank You for placing me in a church where the Lord is worshipped, and His people are changed and where I have been changed for the better.

With praise and thanksgiving, they sang to the Lord: He is good
Ezra 3:11 NCV

Day 32 Morning

Check all of your existing blessings:

☐ Health ☐ Shelter ☐ Food ☐ Clothing ☐ Family ☐ Life

In addition to the above, today I am grateful for...

With praise and thanksgiving, they sang to the Lord: He is good

Ezra 3:11 NCV

Day 32 Evening

As I close this day, I am truly Grateful for..

Write below anyone who blessed you with Kindness today.

-------------------------------------   ------------------------------------

-------------------------------------   ------------------------------------

-------------------------------------   ------------------------------------

How did you express to them your Gratitude?

With praise and thanksgiving, they sang to the Lord: He is good
Ezra 3:11 NCV

Day 33

Dear God,

I come to you to say thank you for my mom's healing. This has been a very difficult and scary year for my family. With mom being sick and helping with my grandma, back and forth to the hospital and recovering from my own surgery I know for sure that it was you carrying me along the way and I am so thankful. It brings me great comfort to know that I can cast all my worries and anxiety upon you because you care form me. Thank you for all that you have done and continue to do.

Sing to the Lord and praise his name; every day tell how he saves us.
Psalm 96:2 NCV

Day 33 Morning

Check all of your existing blessings:

☐ *Health* ☐ *Shelter* ☐ *Food* ☐ *Clothing* ☐ *Family* ☐ *Life*

In addition to the above, today I am grateful for..

Sing to the Lord and praise his name; every day tell how he saves us.
Psalm 96:2 NCV

Day 33 Evening

As I close this day, I am truly Grateful for...

Write below anyone who blessed you with Kindness today.

----------------------------------   ----------------------------------

----------------------------------   ----------------------------------

----------------------------------   ----------------------------------

How did you express to them your Gratitude?

Sing to the Lord and praise his name; every day tell how he saves us.
Psalm 96:2 NCV

Day 34

Bless your Holy name, Father, God!!!
You faithfully bless me day in and day out. Lord I am endlessly grateful! As I begin to start my business day, the very first email that I saw this morning was pertaining to a life changing opportunity for me concerning my book! Really, God? Life Changing is actually an understatement! Me? Do you mean to tell me that I will be seated amongst Executives, Fortune 500 Company Leadership?? You have chosen an ordinary servant to do an extraordinary assignment. Thank You, Father! If I had a thousand tongues, I could not thank you enough!!!

Sacrifice thank offerings to God, fulfill your vows to the Most High
Psalm 50:14 NIV

Day 34 Morning

Check all of your existing blessings:

☐ Health   ☐ Shelter   ☐ Food   ☐ Clothing   ☐ Family   ☐ Life

In addition to the above, today I am grateful for...

Sacrifice thank offerings to God, fulfill your vows to the Most High
Psalm 50:14 NIV

Day 34 Evening

As I close this day, I am truly Grateful for...

Write below anyone who blessed you with Kindness today.

-------------------------------------   -------------------------------------

-------------------------------------   -------------------------------------

-------------------------------------   -------------------------------------

How did you express to them your Gratitude?

Sacrifice thank offerings to God, fulfill your vows to the Most High
Psalm 50:14 NIV

Day 35

You are an amazing God! My heart was aching four days ago as I noticed family members on social media publicly denouncing another member for her exceptionally bad behavior. However, I know she suffers greatly from mental illness and I remembered her when she was just my sweet younger cousin, whom looked up to me and who grew to become a beautiful young woman who did well in college and made funny jokes.

Father, I am no longer as close to my family as I once was, never the less, I went out on a limb and suggested to each one that they pray for her, as I have been on my knees, tears flowing and bringing her issues to You on the throne. I was in amazement seeing our entire family begin to show compassion, pray and weep for her! Father they were lifting up her name up to YOU! Never would I have ever imagined witnessing that! I Love you, God, you are so faithful, and I am certain that it is already done!

I will give thee thanks in the great congregation: I will praise thee among much people.
Psalm 35:18 KJV

Day 35 Morning

Check all of your existing blessings:

☐ Health ☐ Shelter ☐ Food ☐ Clothing ☐ Family ☐ Life

In addition to the above, today I am grateful for...

I will give thee thanks in the great congregation: I will praise thee among much people.
Psalm 35:18 KJV

Day 35 Evening

As I close this day, I am truly Grateful for...

Write below anyone who blessed you with Kindness today.

-------------------------------------   -------------------------------------

-------------------------------------   -------------------------------------

-------------------------------------   -------------------------------------

How did you express to them your Gratitude?

I will give thee thanks in the great congregation: I will praise thee among much people.
Psalm 35:18 KJV

Day 36

Father,

I've been dealing with a set of circumstances at my job that has made it challenging and at times unbearable to be at work. The constant negativity in speech and deeds has been overwhelming. However, today you reminded me that my strength is wrapped up, tied up and tangled up in you. You reminded me that everything will work out for the good of those who love You and are called according to Your purpose. You reminded me that trials produce endurance and an opportunity to grow. A reminder is a blessing and I thank you, God, your reminder helped me to change my perspective which has changed my reality. Now I give my energy to the things I can change and I refuse to give my energy those things and situations I have no control over. Today, I can move forward in Peace.

I always thank my God for you because of the grace God has given you in Christ Jesus.
1 Corinthians 1:4

Day 36 Morning

Check all of your existing blessings:

☐ Health ☐ Shelter ☐ Food ☐ Clothing ☐ Family ☐ Life

In addition to the above, today I am grateful for...

\---
\---
\---
\---
\---
\---
\---
\---
\---
\---
\---
\---
\---
\---
\---
\---

I always thank my God for you because of the grace God has given you in Christ Jesus.
1 Corinthians 1:4

Day 36 Evening

As I close this day, I am truly Grateful for...

Write below anyone who blessed you with Kindness today.

-------------------------------------   -------------------------------------

-------------------------------------   -------------------------------------

-------------------------------------   -------------------------------------

How did you express to them your Gratitude?

I always thank my God for you because of the grace God has given you in Christ Jesus.
1 Corinthians 1:4

Day 37

Lord,

Thank you for the unimaginable peace that has returned to engulf my home. My household has encountered strife of many kinds. This strife caused much disconnection, mistrust and almost dismantled the love that existed. Oh but God! I thank you for stepping in right on time! You took away the pain and cultivated new love, peace, joy, respect and admiration. I love you Lord and I thank you. I will spend the rest of my days worshipping and praising you along with witnessing to others about you.

Let them offer sacrifices to thank him. With joy they should tell what he has done.

Psalm 107:22

Day 37 Morning

Check all of your existing blessings:

☐ Health ☐ Shelter ☐ Food ☐ Clothing ☐ Family ☐ Life

In addition to the above, today I am grateful for...

Let them offer sacrifices to thank him. With joy they should tell what he has done.

Psalm 107:22

Day 37 Evening

As I close this day, I am truly Grateful for..

Write below anyone who blessed you with Kindness today.

---------------------------------------   ---------------------------------------

---------------------------------------   ---------------------------------------

---------------------------------------   ---------------------------------------

How did you express to them your Gratitude?

Let them offer sacrifices to thank him. With joy they should tell what he has done.

Psalm 107:22

Day 38

Lord thank you for my sister! For the past couple years, she has almost single-handedly been the primary care giver for our mother and grandmother. Although she has a husband, two children and a full-time job and household to care for…she manages to carry the day to day and needs of another household on her broad shoulders. She has sacrificed much time and money without complaining. You placed a special heart in her and I'm grateful that people like her still exist in the world today. Thank you, God, for the many rewards you grant her because of her unselfishness. It's as if you said "Daughter, because you have proved your love for Me, your wish is my command." God, you are better than I ever imagined, thank you.

You will sing and make music to the Lord with your hearts
Ephesians 5:19 ISV

Day 38 Morning

Check all of your existing blessings:

☐ Health ☐ Shelter ☐ Food ☐ Clothing ☐ Family ☐ Life

In addition to the above, today I am grateful for...

You will sing and make music to the Lord with your hearts
Ephesians 5:19 ISV

Day 38 Evening

As I close this day, I am truly Grateful for...

Write below anyone who blessed you with Kindness today.

-----------------------------------   -----------------------------------

-----------------------------------   -----------------------------------

-----------------------------------   -----------------------------------

How did you express to them your Gratitude?

You will sing and make music to the Lord with your hearts
Ephesians 5:19 ISV

Day 39

Lord,

Thank you for people who are kind with their words and sincerity. Today, I faced a major challenge. I was due to get a health procedure completed; however, as the process was about to start, I got extremely nervous and opted out because of fear. I left the medical facility feeling defeated; however, you guided me to a place of refuge. I explained to a couple of friends what happened. They didn't make fun of me nor did they judge me. Their words, prayers and conversation really helped and meant so much to me. So after months of delay, today I submitted my will and got the procedure completed. Thank you for your patience with me Lord, for I'm learning that You will direct my path as long as I allow you to have your way in my life.

Every good gift and every perfect gift is from above
James 1:17 ESV

Day 39 Morning

Check all of your existing blessings:

☐ Health ☐ Shelter ☐ Food ☐ Clothing ☐ Family ☐ Life

In addition to the above, today I am grateful for..

_____

_____

_____

_____

_____

_____

_____

_____

_____

_____

_____

_____

_____

_____

_____

Every good gift and every perfect gift is from above
James 1:17 ESV

Day 39 Evening

As I close this day, I am truly Grateful for..

Write below anyone who blessed you with Kindness today.

-------------------------------------   -------------------------------------

-------------------------------------   -------------------------------------

-------------------------------------   -------------------------------------

How did you express to them your Gratitude?

Every good gift and every perfect gift is from above
James 1:17 ESV

Day 40

Father,

I come to you grateful and embarrassed at the same time. Today, while driving I did the unthinkable.... I dozed off behind the wheel, not once but twice. Because of your grace and mercy, you awakened me both times. The first time you prevented me from merging into oncoming traffic. The second time you prevented me from running into a ditch on the side of the road. Both of these situations could have taken my life, but you said No. Thank you for caring for me better than I care for myself.

A Psalm of thanksgiving. Shout with joy to the LORD, all the earth!
Psalm 100:1 NLT

Day 40 Morning

Check all of your existing blessings:

☐ *Health* ☐ *Shelter* ☐ *Food* ☐ *Clothing* ☐ *Family* ☐ *Life*

In addition to the above, today I am grateful for...

A Psalm of thanksgiving. Shout with joy to the LORD, all the earth!
Psalm 100:1 NLT

Day 40 Evening

As I close this day, I am truly Grateful for…………………………………………

_____

_____

_____

_____

_____

_____

_____

_____

_____

_____

Write below anyone who blessed you with Kindness today.

_____   _____

_____   _____

_____   _____

How did you express to them your Gratitude?

_____

_____

_____

_____

_____

_____

A Psalm of thanksgiving. Shout with joy to the LORD, all the earth!
Psalm 100:1 NLT

Day 41

Jesus,

Thank you for blessing my youngest child with a breakthrough in his Algebra 1 homework assignment today. While attempting to do the assignment on his own, he became extremely frustrated because he didn't understand the concept, yet he continued to try and figure it out. With minimal guidance, I was able to point him in the right direction and he completed his assignment accurately. Thank you for showing up and preventing him from being and feeling defeated. Thank you for being Jehovah-Jireh, The Lord Provider.

May he give you the desire of your heart and make all your plans succeed.

Psalm 20:4 NIV

Day 41 Morning

Check all of your existing blessings:

☐ Health ☐ Shelter ☐ Food ☐ Clothing ☐ Family ☐ Life

In addition to the above, today I am grateful for...

May he give you the desire of your heart and make all your plans succeed.
Psalm 20:4 NIV

Day 41 Evening

As I close this day, I am truly Grateful for...

Write below anyone who blessed you with Kindness today.

--------------------------------------   --------------------------------------
--------------------------------------   --------------------------------------
--------------------------------------   --------------------------------------

How did you express to them your Gratitude?

May he give you the desire of your heart and make all your plans succeed.
Psalm 20:4 NIV

Day 42

Lord I thank you for the deliverance, transformation and submission of my husband unto you. His past behaviors have opened the door for divorce; however, we have been able to work through it. Lord, he is now in a place where he intentionally chooses healthy and God-honoring activities. He no longer gives into habits that are questionable or displeasing to you. Lord, he's able to walk in freedom, integrity and happiness. Thank you for his freedom to live righteous and holy because he yields to your spirit, voice and commands.

I will give you thanks forever!
Psalm 30:13 NLT

Day 42 Morning

Check all of your existing blessings:

☐ Health ☐ Shelter ☐ Food ☐ Clothing ☐ Family ☐ Life

In addition to the above, today I am grateful for...

I will give you thanks forever!
Psalm 30:13 NLT

Day 42 Evening

As I close this day, I am truly Grateful for...

_____

_____

_____

_____

_____

_____

_____

_____

_____

_____

Write below anyone who blessed you with Kindness today.

_____   _____

_____   _____

_____   _____

How did you express to them your Gratitude?

_____

_____

_____

_____

_____

I will give you thanks forever!
Psalm 30:13 NLT

Day 43

Eighteen months prior to the death of my daughter Tisha, God you gave me a tremendous amount of Scriptures. Over the course of time reading the scriptures I would ask you Lord what this is about. You said to me you will understand later. At that time, I did not question you anymore. However, I never knew you were preparing me for the death of my beloved daughter. Thinking back, one scripture stands out amongst the rest. Lamentations 3:32 NKJV "Though He causes grief, Yet He will show you compassion according to the multitude of His mercies."

Lord I thank you that the evidence of your compassion showed up in my life. I Thank you, for you alone gave me so much peace. Now Lord I utterly understand what it means to have peace that surpasses ALL UNDERSTANDING. Lord I thank you for allowing be to be a comfort to my family during this time. I thank you for not allowing me to be bitter or angry towards you. You even allowed me to praise you in the mist of the hurt. You gave me such strength. I am still thanking you today for the strength that you have given me. Lord I know I did not lose my mind because of the relationship I have with you. I know how important it is to have Faith in you regardless to what it looks like and regardless to what it feels like.

Your word says you will never leave me nor forsake me, and again the proof of your Word and Your Love consistently shows up in my life. I know that your Love is AMAZING and so are You. Lord I thank You for Breathing for me when I could not figure out how to breathe during this season of my *life.*

I thank you for all the preparation that you had in place for me. I thank you for allowing me to know that there is life after death. Lord even the days that my heart misses her touch her smell her smile her laughter, you comfort me. You do not allow depression, nor do you allow the enemy to attack my mind. Lord I thank you that your Word says when I am weak you are strong. Lord, I thank you for you. I thank you for being all that I need. Lord I that you for being evident in my life. I thank you when people ask, "How are you so strong?" I can boldly say, **Jesus**! Thank you so much God. You even sent angels in my life that did what you ask of them. Thank you for showing me so much favor. Lord I thank you for loving me and not being shame of showing your love toward me. Thank you for carrying me when I felt like I could not take another step. Your love for me would not let me fall. Thank You!

Thank YOU for being My AWESOME GOD

I will speak highly of you, my God and King, and I will bless your name forever and ever.
Psalm 145:1 ISV

Day 43 Morning

Check all of your existing blessings:

☐ Health ☐ Shelter ☐ Food ☐ Clothing ☐ Family ☐ Life

In addition to the above, today I am grateful for..

I will speak highly of you, my God and King, and I will bless your name forever and ever.
Psalm 145:1 ISV

Day 43 Evening

As I close this day, I am truly Grateful for...

Write below anyone who blessed you with Kindness today.

--   --

--   --

--   --

How did you express to them your Gratitude?

I will speak highly of you, my God and King, and I will bless your name forever and ever.
Psalm 145:1 ISV

Day 44

God...my Father,

Thank you for bringing healing to my skin! The adult acne had been really wearing on me out emotionally. The consistent breakouts and blemishes began to affect my self-esteem. I remember petitioning you for skin that was clear, acne free, oil-controlled and healthy. I desired skin that naturally radiated. I noticed last week that my old breakouts were gone, and no new ones had formed. However, today while washing my face, you nudged me to really take a look at my skin in the mirror. WOW Jesus, my skin is radiating! Thank you for answering such a simple prayer that has had a major impact on me emotionally. You are wonderful.

Praise the LORD in song, for He has done excellent things
Isaiah 12:5 NAS

Day 44 Morning

Check all of your existing blessings:

☐ Health ☐ Shelter ☐ Food ☐ Clothing ☐ Family ☐ Life

In addition to the above, today I am grateful for...

Praise the LORD in song, for He has done excellent things
Isaiah 12:5 NAS

Day 44 Evening

As I close this day, I am truly Grateful for...

Write below anyone who blessed you with Kindness today.

---------------------------------------   ---------------------------------------

---------------------------------------   ---------------------------------------

---------------------------------------   ---------------------------------------

How did you express to them your Gratitude?

Praise the LORD in song, for He has done excellent things
Isaiah 12:5 NAS

Day 45

Father, thank you for the ability to share this testimonial with my brother's and sister's. First giving honor to God who is the head of my life.

When I look back over my life, God has most definitely brought me through many times of trials and tribulations. One of the many times that sticks out in my mind the most is when I was 16 years old. It was the summer of 1993; I was riding my bike down the sidewalk and out of nowhere here comes a car and hit me throwing me multiple feet in the air and hitting the pavement face first and bounced. They even tried to leave, I was getting rushed to the hospital in and out of consciousness, we tubes being stuck down my throat IVs started, I seen my life flash before my eyes I was out. In the hospital I'm lying there critically injured broken nose and teeth traumatic brain injury, ruptured spline, fracture pelvic, cuts everywhere, tire track on my leg, over 100 stiches in my face and head. I could hear my Mother asking the nurses and Surgeons is she going to be alright, but I couldn't respond or see anything at this point. I remember my Sisters Telling me you still look beautiful, me not knowing my face was all torn up at the time. After being hospitalized for about a month I wanted to see one day what my face really looked like. I had to get help to the mirror and when I saw my face I just cried, I thought I looked like something out of a horror movie and it really took a toll on me. Thinking I would never look normal again my face was swollen full of cuts and stiches. My Mother and Father assured me that I was still Beautiful no matter what anybody say. My limbs were all jammed up from head to toe. Having to get some of my Mobility back in my legs and to hear the Doctor's say to my Mother she will never be the same Physically just took me out, but here is the good news. When I was laying in the bed and had nowhere to turn, God reached down from heaven and by His grace and mercy saved me. He sealed the deal with His Holy Spirit. Today I can boldly say that God has set me free of the negative talk. God Created Me and I'm So Thankful and Grateful For All He Has Done and Continue To Do For Me. My Transformation hasn't been easy, but with God as My Savior, Guide, Example, Healer, Provider and My Strength. My Faith is strong and I am Definitely Faithful. GLORY HALLELUJAH

I will be glad and rejoice in thee: I will sing praise to thy name, O thou most High.
Psalm 9:2 KJV

Day 45 Morning

Check all of your existing blessings:

☐ Health ☐ Shelter ☐ Food ☐ Clothing ☐ Family ☐ Life

In addition to the above, today I am grateful for……………………………………………

I will be glad and rejoice in thee: I will sing praise to thy name, O thou most High.

Psalm 9:2 KJV

Day 45 Evening

As I close this day, I am truly Grateful for...

Write below anyone who blessed you with Kindness today.

-------------------------------------   -------------------------------------

-------------------------------------   -------------------------------------

-------------------------------------   -------------------------------------

How did you express to them your Gratitude?

I will be glad and rejoice in thee: I will sing praise to thy name, O thou most High.
Psalm 9:2 KJV

Day 46

Dear God, I thank you for the people you strategically placed in my life. Who knew that a simple visit to a church would forever change my relationship with you...? well of course, you did :). Thank you for putting me exactly where I needed to be when I was not strong enough to figure it out on my own. Thank you for continuing to guide my steps ensuring I stay on the path you have designated for me. Thank you for helping me submit to you driving the wheel of my life, even when I thought my directions were better. Lord, I am learning to truly give you total control. Thank you for your tolerance as I strive to get this spiritual relationship right, because when I get that I get you and when I get you I get EVERYTHING!!!

God saved you by his grace when you believed.
Ephesians 2:8 NLT

Day 46 Morning

Check all of your existing blessings:

☐ Health ☐ Shelter ☐ Food ☐ Clothing ☐ Family ☐ Life

In addition to the above, today I am grateful for...

God saved you by his grace when you believed.
Ephesians 2:8 NLT

Day 46 Evening

As I close this day, I am truly Grateful for...

Write below anyone who blessed you with Kindness today.

------------------------------------   ------------------------------------

------------------------------------   ------------------------------------

------------------------------------   ------------------------------------

How did you express to them your Gratitude?

God saved you by his grace when you believed.
Ephesians 2:8 NLT

Day 47

Morning Father,

Today I want to thank you for my spiritual father and the first family. Thank you because they are truly after your heart. Thank you for the numerous sacrifices they make for the kingdom, even when it has a negative impact on their personal lives. I ask that you return unto them 100-fold every sacrifice they have made big or small. Let the things in their life be for your glory but for their good. You know the desires of their heart so fulfill those things. Let them have nothing lacking, missing, or broken. Let your favor surround them so that everything that they touch will prosper. Thank you for the loving word pastor is able to give week after week. Not only does he teach the word, but he gives us principles on how we can make it work in our life and more importantly he is an example of the principles at work. Thank you for leading me to a place where I can be spiritually fed when I didn't even know there was a hunger to be satisfied. Thank you for who they are and all that they do. I just ask that you enlarge their territory. Strengthen and renew them daily so they do not become weak or weary to carry out their assignment. All these things I ask and thank you in your precious son Jesus name, Amen.

I thank my God every time I remember you
Philippians 1:3 NCV

Day 47 Morning

Check all of your existing blessings:

☐ Health ☐ Shelter ☐ Food ☐ Clothing ☐ Family ☐ Life

In addition to the above, today I am grateful for...

I thank my God every time I remember you
Philippians 1:3 NCV

Day 47 Evening

As I close this day, I am truly Grateful for...

Write below anyone who blessed you with Kindness today.

-------------------------------------   -------------------------------------

-------------------------------------   -------------------------------------

-------------------------------------   -------------------------------------

How did you express to them your Gratitude?

I thank my God every time I remember you
Philippians 1:3 NCV

Day 48

Lord

Thank you for using me. You are daily showing me how to take who I am, who I want to be and what I can do, and use it for a purpose greater than myself! Lord you said that everything got started in you… and finds its purpose in you. I'm truly grateful that you have given me a strong desire to live the purpose you created for me. Show me my design and how my talents can best serve your kingdom. Lord, my heart is so happy because you are teaching me to lean upon your understanding and not my own. You are filling me with a thirst and hunger for you. You are making your word as essential to me as air. Lord draw nearer to you is my hearts outcry. Lord, as I'm learning to walk upright, allowing you to renew my mind heart and spirit to reflect your image, transforming my tastes and desires so I'm not overcome by temptation I'm able to draw others into your kingdom because I display the privileges of being your child. Thank you for being with me throughout the day as my sovereign blanket of protection. In Jesus name, I'm grateful.

I will praise you every day; yes, I will praise you forever.

Psalm 145:2

Day 48 Morning

Check all of your existing blessings:

☐ Health ☐ Shelter ☐ Food ☐ Clothing ☐ Family ☐ Life

In addition to the above, today I am grateful for...

I will praise you every day; yes, I will praise you forever.
Psalm 145:2

Day 48 Evening

As I close this day, I am truly Grateful for..

Write below anyone who blessed you with Kindness today.

-------------------------------------   -------------------------------------

-------------------------------------   -------------------------------------

-------------------------------------   -------------------------------------

How did you express to them your Gratitude?

I will praise you every day; yes, I will praise you forever.

Psalm 145:2

Day 49

Lord,

I thank you for the simple things you turnaround to work in my favor. My babysitting schedule inter-fered with my evening school schedule this week. Although I needed the income, I knew I would have to forfeit it for school. My past response to disappointment was to worry. However, I decided I would give you my cares and concerns. I stated aloud "Lord if it's your will then you will change things around." Within 24 hours you did just that! My babysitting schedule changed from nights to days! Lord, thank you for showing up in my situation. You make me feel like your beloved daughter.

Great is the LORD and most worthy of praise
Psalm 145:3 NIV

Day 49 Morning

Check all of your existing blessings:

☐ Health ☐ Shelter ☐ Food ☐ Clothing ☐ Family ☐ Life

In addition to the above, today I am grateful for...

Great is the LORD and most worthy of praise
Psalm 145:3 NIV

Day 49 Evening

As I close this day, I am truly Grateful for...

Write below anyone who blessed you with Kindness today.

--------------------------------------   --------------------------------------

--------------------------------------   --------------------------------------

--------------------------------------   --------------------------------------

How did you express to them your Gratitude?

Great is the LORD and most worthy of praise
Psalm 145:3 NIV

Day 50

The effectual fervent prayer of a righteous man availeth much. Today, I found out that a group of righteous women in our church took it upon themselves to join and lift me, their First Lady, up in prayer. They prayed 30 consecutive days for every area of my life. Lord, I thank you for kindly placing me on their hearts and I thank you for their obedience to your call. Lord, I also want to thank you for answering their prayers because I feel the love, strength, encouragement, healing and favor that only you are able to give. Jesus, I am grateful for your demonstration of faithfulness and unconditional love towards me.

All of your works will thank you, LORD, and your faithful followers will praise you.
Psalm 145:10 NLT

Day 50 Morning

Check all of your existing blessings:

☐ *Health* ☐ *Shelter* ☐ *Food* ☐ *Clothing* ☐ *Family* ☐ *Life*

In addition to the above, today I am grateful for...

\---
\---
\---
\---
\---
\---
\---
\---
\---
\---
\---
\---
\---
\---
\---

All of your works will thank you, LORD, and your faithful followers will praise you.
Psalm 145:10 NLT

Day 50 Evening

As I close this day, I am truly Grateful for...

Write below anyone who blessed you with Kindness today.

-------------------------------------   -------------------------------------

-------------------------------------   -------------------------------------

-------------------------------------   -------------------------------------

How did you express to them your Gratitude?

All of your works will thank you, LORD, and your faithful followers will praise you.
Psalm 145:10 NLT

Day 51

Dear God,

I am truly grateful today because I can honestly say that I have forgiven a past hurt. 6 years ago, my husband was unfaithful and his behavior resulted in the birth of a child. Devastated, disgusted, hurt and enraged were only a few emotions I felt. I literally had hate in my heart. I would pretend I was okay, but I was dying inside. Because I loved my husband, I was willing to make our marriage work.

Lord, you really stepped into both of our lives and carefully guided us back to you and one another. You showed me how to trust. You taught me how to believe in you and your word. Your Holy Word and Presence comforted me every time I needed you. You diminished my tears into laughter. You resuscitated my heart so I could unconditionally love again. I love my husband more today and I am in love with him more than ever because you poured life into our dead marriage. God, you turned my ashes into beauty just like you promised. Thank You!

My mouth will speak in praise of the LORD. Let every creature praise his holy name for ever and ever.
Psalm 145:21 NIV

Day 51 Morning

Check all of your existing blessings:

☐ Health   ☐ Shelter   ☐ Food   ☐ Clothing   ☐ Family   ☐ Life

In addition to the above, today I am grateful for...

My mouth will speak in praise of the LORD. Let every creature praise his holy name for ever and ever.
Psalm 145:21 NIV

Day 51 Evening

As I close this day, I am truly Grateful for...

Write below anyone who blessed you with Kindness today.

--------------------------------------   --------------------------------------

--------------------------------------   --------------------------------------

--------------------------------------   --------------------------------------

How did you express to them your Gratitude?

My mouth will speak in praise of the LORD. Let every creature praise his holy name for ever and ever.
Psalm 145:21 NIV

Day 52

Lord,

I want to thank you for the miracle you performed for my daughter. 2 months ago, my grandson's father had our local Sheriff Department served us papers for full custody papers. My daughter is an excellent mother, works hard daily to support her child. This custody battle brought many negative feelings towards the father. The thought of losing custody devastated my daughter and our household. However, we put our trust and faith in God.

Today in court, Lord you showed us favor. Not only did my daughter retain full custody, but also the judge ordered that the father begin paying child support immediately! God, this was your battle at the onset. Thank you for being our battle-axe in our time of trouble. We love you.

Giving thanks through him to God the Father.
Colossians 3:17 NLT

Day 52 Morning

Check all of your existing blessings:

☐ Health ☐ Shelter ☐ Food ☐ Clothing ☐ Family ☐ Life

In addition to the above, today I am grateful for..

Giving thanks through him to God the Father.
Colossians 3:17 NLT

Day 52 Evening

As I close this day, I am truly Grateful for...

Write below anyone who blessed you with Kindness today.

-------------------------------------   -------------------------------------

-------------------------------------   -------------------------------------

-------------------------------------   -------------------------------------

How did you express to them your Gratitude?

Giving thanks through him to God the Father.
Colossians 3:17 NLT

Day 53

Gracious God,

Thank you for sparing the lives of my sister and nephew. Both were involved in serious car accidents two weeks apart. The accidents destroyed both vehicles and left them without cars; however, they walked away with their lives and made a full recovery. Thank you for your grace and mercy.

Thanks be to God, who delivers me through Jesus Christ our Lord!
Romans 7:25 NCV

Day 53 Morning

Check all of your existing blessings:

☐ Health ☐ Shelter ☐ Food ☐ Clothing ☐ Family ☐ Life

In addition to the above, today I am grateful for...

Thanks be to God, who delivers me through Jesus Christ our Lord!
Romans 7:25 NCV

Day 53 Evening

As I close this day, I am truly Grateful for..

Write below anyone who blessed you with Kindness today.

------------------------------------   ------------------------------------

------------------------------------   ------------------------------------

------------------------------------   ------------------------------------

How did you express to them your Gratitude?

Thanks be to God, who delivers me through Jesus Christ our Lord!
Romans 7:25 NCV

Day 54

Today, I went to get my oil changed. While waiting, the service advisor informed me I needed to replace one of my tires. Due to my financial situation, I told him I could not afford a new tire along with the oil change. Therefore, he said he would give me a complimentary oil change if I paid for the tire because he believes safety is first. I was able to walk away with an oil change and a new tire. God, I thank you for blessing me today.

Tell God what you need, and thank him for all he has done.
Philippians 4:6 NLT

Day 54 Morning

Check all of your existing blessings:

☐ Health ☐ Shelter ☐ Food ☐ Clothing ☐ Family ☐ Life

In addition to the above, today I am grateful for...

Tell God what you need, and thank him for all he has done.
Philippians 4:6 NLT

Day 54 Evening

As I close this day, I am truly Grateful for..

_____

_____

_____

_____

_____

_____

_____

_____

_____

_____

Write below anyone who blessed you with Kindness today.

_____   _____

_____   _____

_____   _____

How did you express to them your Gratitude?

_____

_____

_____

_____

_____

_____

Tell God what you need, and thank him for all he has done.
Philippians 4:6 NLT

Day 55

Not long ago, I was at my lowest. I found myself unemployed, semi-homeless and if it could not get worst, I spent a few days in jail because I had two outstanding warrants. In the midst of this storm, Lord I turned to you for direction. You gave me a peace that I could not explain nor comprehend.

Once released from jail, I decided to surrender totally to you Jesus and focus on improving myself. This is when all my blessings began to flow. Today, my story is drastically different. While working for a temporary agency, the company hired me permanently. I now have my own apartment in spite of an eviction on my record. Finally, you blessed me with my dream car, which enabled me to travel during the holidays to see my family; whom I have not seen in three years. Regardless to my circumstances, you had a plan for me and I know the best is yet to come. I am beyond grateful to you God, for you have performed miracles in my life. I vow never to give up on you. I will always trust and believe that you have my life in your best interest. Thank you for seeing me through and never leaving my side.

Therefore I will give thanks to You, O LORD, among the nations, And I will sing praises to Your name.
2 Samuel 22:50 NAS

Day 55 Morning

Check all of your existing blessings:

☐ *Health* ☐ *Shelter* ☐ *Food* ☐ *Clothing* ☐ *Family* ☐ *Life*

In addition to the above, today I am grateful for…………………………………………

Therefore I will give thanks to You, O LORD, among the nations, And I will sing praises to Your name.
2 Samuel 22:50 NAS

Day 55 Evening

As I close this day, I am truly Grateful for...

Write below anyone who blessed you with Kindness today.

--------------------------------------   --------------------------------------

--------------------------------------   --------------------------------------

--------------------------------------   --------------------------------------

How did you express to them your Gratitude?

Therefore I will give thanks to You, O LORD, among the nations, And I will sing praises to Your name.
2 Samuel 22:50 NAS

Day 56

I am thankful to you God for freeing me from a toxic relationship. This was a relationship I went back to after being separated over a year and a half. Although I knew he didn't mean me any good, I went back. I tricked myself into thinking he would change. With him I drunk more, just trying to follow him. Lord, I thank you because as of today, it's been one month since I Have taken a drink of alcohol. Although it may not seem long but it is a milestone for me because I found myself getting drunk everyday as well as on the weekends. Months from now, I will be able to declare I stayed the course, God took away the desire and I am more than a conqueror. Hallelujah

I will sing to the LORD because he has been good to me.

Psalm 13:6 GWT

Day 56 Morning

Check all of your existing blessings:

☐ Health ☐ Shelter ☐ Food ☐ Clothing ☐ Family ☐ Life

In addition to the above, today I am grateful for...

I will sing to the LORD because he has been good to me.
Psalm 13:6 GWT

Day 56 Evening

As I close this day, I am truly Grateful for…………………………………………

Write below anyone who blessed you with Kindness today.

-----------------------------------   --

-----------------------------------   --

-----------------------------------   --

How did you express to them your Gratitude?

I will sing to the LORD because he has been good to me.
Psalm 13:6 GWT

Day 57

Father, I thank you for blessing me in my obedience. I received a job offer in March 2020 but due to covid-19 I was not able to start the job until May 2020. God blessed me with couple who were church members who lived around the corner from me. Due to unemployment, I didn't have much including transportation. Our of the goodness of their heart, the wife was able to take me to get my finger-prints, which was required for the job. Great news! Once I began working, the job paid me enough to get a new water heater, a new central water line, a new furnace and two new doors on the back of my garage that were badly needed. This was all done within 6 months! To God be the Glory

Raising my voice in thanksgiving and telling about Your wonderful works.
Psalm 26:7 HCS

Day 57 Morning

Check all of your existing blessings:

☐ Health ☐ Shelter ☐ Food ☐ Clothing ☐ Family ☐ Life

In addition to the above, today I am grateful for...

Raising my voice in thanksgiving and telling about Your wonderful works.
Psalm 26:7 HCS

Day 57 Evening

As I close this day, I am truly Grateful for...

Write below anyone who blessed you with Kindness today.

-------------------------------------   -------------------------------------

-------------------------------------   -------------------------------------

-------------------------------------   -------------------------------------

How did you express to them your Gratitude?

Raising my voice in thanksgiving and telling about Your wonderful works.
Psalm 26:7 HCS

Day 58

Father,

thank you for restoring and strengthening the affection and bond between my firstborn daughter and myself. I Love my daughter and I am grateful that you stepped in and changed a relationship that looked doomed to the natural eye. I have spent many nights in the past yearning over what seemed like an impossible healing, however, the moment I declared things anew in YOU; I began to see fresh life. Like a whirlwind my chains were broken! Our relationship is now better than I could have imagined in my wildest dreams!

Sing unto the LORD, O you saints of his, and give thanks at the remembrance of his holiness.
Psalm 30:4 KJV

Day 58 Morning

Check all of your existing blessings:

☐ Health   ☐ Shelter   ☐ Food   ☐ Clothing   ☐ Family   ☐ Life

In addition to the above, today I am grateful for…………………………………………

Sing unto the LORD, O you saints of his, and give thanks at the remembrance of his holiness.
Psalm 30:4 KJV

Day 58 Evening

As I close this day, I am truly Grateful for...

_____

_____

_____

_____

_____

_____

_____

_____

_____

_____

Write below anyone who blessed you with Kindness today.

_____   _____

_____   _____

_____   _____

How did you express to them your Gratitude?

_____

_____

_____

_____

_____

_____

Sing unto the LORD, O you saints of his, and give thanks at the remembrance of his holiness.
Psalm 30:4 KJV

Day 59

Dear God,

This is your daughter coming to you in gratitude for the help you provided me. At 5 p.m. I petitioned you about my rent, which was due today in the amount of $865. I absolutely didn't know where the money was going to come from, but I knew you would make a way out of no way. Lord at 6p.m. one of my dance students' parents informed me she received her student loan money today and would like to pay $500 in advance for the school dance year. At 6:30 p.m. another parent came and re-minded me she owed me $400 in past due fees. She stated she didn't have the full $400, but she has $366 right now and she would pay the balance next week. Lord, I needed $865 and you gave me $866. You made a way out of no way and all I can say is THANK YOU GOD!!!!!

Blessed be the Lord, who daily loadeth us with benefits
Psalm 68:19 KJV

Day 59 Morning

Check all of your existing blessings:

☐ Health ☐ Shelter ☐ Food ☐ Clothing ☐ Family ☐ Life

n addition to the above, today I am grateful for...

Blessed be the Lord, who daily loadeth us with benefits
Psalm 68:19 KJV

Day 59 Evening

As I close this day, I am truly Grateful for...

Write below anyone who blessed you with Kindness today.

------------------------------------   ------------------------------------

------------------------------------   ------------------------------------

------------------------------------   ------------------------------------

How did you express to them your Gratitude?

Blessed be the Lord, who daily loadeth us with benefits
Psalm 68:19 KJV

Day 60

Dear God,

Thank you for my new commercial property, it is perfect! Exactly 90 days ago, I received a letter that my Landlord was selling my commercial property and I would have 90 days to find a new commercial space to relocate my business. My prayer to you was "Dear God, I don't know the plans you have for me, but I trust you. Please order my steps." Thank you for placing me in a better location with a better lease agreement. You are so good to me. Thank you.

Then we your people, the sheep of your pasture, will thank you forever and ever
Psalm 79:13 NLT

Day 60 Morning

Check all of your existing blessings:

☐ *Health* ☐ *Shelter* ☐ *Food* ☐ *Clothing* ☐ *Family* ☐ *Life*

In addition to the above, today I am grateful for..

Then we your people, the sheep of your pasture, will thank you forever and ever
Psalm 79:13 NLT

Day 60 Evening

As I close this day, I am truly Grateful for..

_____
_____
_____
_____
_____
_____
_____
_____
_____
_____

Write below anyone who blessed you with Kindness today.

_____   _____

_____   _____

_____   _____

How did you express to them your Gratitude?

_____
_____
_____
_____
_____
_____

Then we your people, the sheep of your pasture, will thank you forever and ever
Psalm 79:13 NLT

Day 61

Dear Father, my relationship with my husband has been rocky for a year. It is such a terrible feeling to marry the love of your life only to believe the union is headed towards divorce. Today is my birthday and I am not expecting anything. In my heart, Lord all I want is for my marriage to be renewed. To my surprise, my husband, took me to dinner and told me "our relationship" has been heavy on his heart and he would like for us to go to Christian Counseling. Thank you God, You have given me the best birthday gift ever!

I rise at midnight to thank you for your just regulations.
Psalm 119:62 NLT

Day 61 Morning

☐ Health ☐ Shelter ☐ Food ☐ Clothing ☐ Family ☐ Life

n addition to the above, today I am grateful for...

I rise at midnight to thank you for your just regulations.
Psalm 119:62 NLT

Day 61 Evening

As I close this day, I am truly Grateful for..

Write below anyone who blessed you with Kindness today.

-------------------------------------   -------------------------------------
-------------------------------------   -------------------------------------
-------------------------------------   -------------------------------------

How did you express to them your Gratitude?

I rise at midnight to thank you for your just regulations.
Psalm 119:62 NLT

Day 62

Father, thank you for your kindness and mercy! I must share how good You Lord has been to our family. We have a daughter in Atlanta who recently purchased a new home. In early mid-November, my husband and I travelled to help with the move and assist with our granddaughter. As you know, the COVID numbers are quite high in Atlanta. We took all the necessary precautions and pretty much just stayed in, packing and organizing the move and caring for our grandchild. We returned to Kansas City and two days later, our son tested positive. He was extremely ill. The remaining members of our family bubble tested, and we all were negative with the exception of our daughter. It is amazing that God would send us to Georgia, a hot spot for COVID-19, to protect us. As you know, my husband is battling through stage 4 chronic kidney disease and for us to not have caught COVID-19 is a BIG HALLELUJAH HERE FOR HIS SAKE! Our son and daughter seem to have relatively mild cases but still quite ill. We are grateful we are able to care for both of them as God strengthens us. I just wanted to share with you the MARVELOUS blessings God has bestowed on us. Thank you for all your encouragement and pouring the word into the Sisters.

Give thanks to the God of heaven. His love endures forever.
Psalm 136:26 NIV

Day 62 Morning

Check all of your existing blessings:

☐ *Health* ☐ *Shelter* ☐ *Food* ☐ *Clothing* ☐ *Family* ☐ *Life*

In addition to the above, today I am grateful for...

Give thanks to the God of heaven. His love endures forever.
Psalm 136:26 NIV

Day 62 Evening

As I close this day, I am truly Grateful for...

Write below anyone who blessed you with Kindness today.

-----------------------------------   -----------------------------------

-----------------------------------   -----------------------------------

-----------------------------------   -----------------------------------

How did you express to them your Gratitude?

Give thanks to the God of heaven. His love endures forever.
Psalm 136:26 NIV

Day 63

Lord this has been one of the most challenging years of my adult life. Events of this year challenged me, confused me, stretched me and hurt me. Jesus, in spite of it all, your love kept me together. Your Presence became a reality to me like never before. I thank you for the times I was able to turn to you when I could not turn to anyone else. Although this year was hard, I learned many lessons. I became a better person and my spiritual development skyrocketed. I can finally say I know what it means to trust and have faith in you. I finally know what you mean when you say count all of our trials and tribulations as joy because they are doing a great work in us. I could not have survived this year without you God. My communication with you is priceless and I'm grateful. I now know what it means to have a personal intimate relationship with you.

Surely the righteous shall give thanks to your name; the upright shall dwell in your presence.
Psalm 140:13 ESV

Day 63 Morning

Check all of your existing blessings:

☐ Health ☐ Shelter ☐ Food ☐ Clothing ☐ Family ☐ Life

In addition to the above, today I am grateful for…………………………………………

Surely the righteous shall give thanks to your name; the upright shall dwell in your presence.
Psalm 140:13 ESV

Day 63 Evening

As I close this day, I am truly Grateful for...

Write below anyone who blessed you with Kindness today.

------------------------------------   ------------------------------------

------------------------------------   ------------------------------------

------------------------------------   ------------------------------------

How did you express to them your Gratitude?

Surely the righteous shall give thanks to your name; the upright shall dwell in your presence.
Psalm 140:13 ESV

Day 64

I'm writing this testimonial in sound mind good health and walking in the fullness of GODS promises. This year has been a test of faith for many of us but how you end a thing is very important. I decided to stand tall and In the midst of a pandemic where most beauty professionals have had to close up shop; I've found myself being called upon for insight at a point I didn't see myself qualified for. For everyone reading this, if you are in any doubt that the Father hears your every cry, I say to you not only does He hear; but at the appointed time He will show up and complete everything He said He would if you faint not. I pray everyone who reads this sees the father in everything. Every Yes and Every NO Is an act of love to demonstrate his good and mercy toward us. Bless you Father for keeping me daily and giving me brand new mercies even when I did not always get it right.

To you, O God of my fathers, I give thanks and praise, for you have given me wisdom and might
Daniel 2:23 ESV

Day 64 Morning

Check all of your existing blessings:

☐ Health ☐ Shelter ☐ Food ☐ Clothing ☐ Family ☐ Life

In addition to the above, today I am grateful for...

To you, O God of my fathers, I give thanks and praise, for you have given me wisdom and might
Daniel 2:23 ESV

Day 64 Evening

As I close this day, I am truly Grateful for...

_____
_____
_____
_____
_____
_____
_____
_____
_____
_____

Write below anyone who blessed you with Kindness today.

_____   _____
_____   _____
_____   _____

How did you express to them your Gratitude?

_____
_____
_____
_____
_____
_____

To you, O God of my fathers, I give thanks and praise, for you have given me wisdom and might
Daniel 2:23 ESV

Day 65

Dear Father in Heaven,

Two weeks ago I went to the ER due to my feet hurting and unable to walk on them. I was sent me home saying it was nothing. I woke up the next morning and was not able to feel my body my stomach on down. I laid in bed the whole day. The next morning, I woke up it was worse. I was weak, not eating, and when I tried, nothing would stay down. I decided to go back to the ER and this time they decided to admit me. Unbeknown to me, my entire body was shutting down on me. After several tes and procedures, we were able to pinpoint some concerns, which were addressed. I am convinced had not God intervened in my healing I could have died. It was God who brought me through all this. I have not got all my feeling back in my body; however, I know by Jesus Strips I am healed in Jesus name. The feeling in my body is slowly coming back and now I am attempting to walk without my walker. I'm just thankful to be alive to tell my story and be back with my children.

Sing out your thanks to the LORD; sing praises to our God with a harp.
Psalm 147:7 NLT

Day 65 Morning

Check all of your existing blessings:

☐ Health ☐ Shelter ☐ Food ☐ Clothing ☐ Family ☐ Life

In addition to the above, today I am grateful for...

Sing out your thanks to the LORD; sing praises to our God with a harp.
Psalm 147:7 NLT

Day 65 Evening

As I close this day, I am truly Grateful for...

Write below anyone who blessed you with Kindness today.

---------------------------------   ---------------------------------

---------------------------------   ---------------------------------

---------------------------------   ---------------------------------

How did you express to them your Gratitude?

Sing out your thanks to the LORD; sing praises to our God with a harp.

Psalm 147:7 NLT

Day 66

Jesus,

Thank you for saving my life! While driving with my sister, a car attempted to run the light, violating our right of traffic. Seeing this unfold in slow motion, I was bracing myself for a hard impact. However, Lord you had different plans. Immediately all vehicles in traffic came to an unexpected and sudden stop. I praise and thank you God. If our vehicle had collided, we would have flipped over several times and landed on the nearby bridge, which could have resulted us losing our lives. Lord, I thank you for my life.

From them will come songs of thanksgiving and the sound of rejoicing.
Jeremiah 30:19 NIV

Day 66 Morning

Check all of your existing blessings:

☐ Health   ☐ Shelter   ☐ Food   ☐ Clothing   ☐ Family   ☐ Life

In addition to the above, today I am grateful for...

From them will come songs of thanksgiving and the sound of rejoicing.
Jeremiah 30:19 NIV

Day 66 Evening

As I close this day, I am truly Grateful for...

_____

_____

_____

_____

_____

_____

_____

_____

Write below anyone who blessed you with Kindness today.

_____   _____

_____   _____

_____   _____

How did you express to them your Gratitude?

_____

_____

_____

_____

_____

From them will come songs of thanksgiving and the sound of rejoicing.
Jeremiah 30:19 NIV

Day 67

So at the beginning of the year I applied for a position that I knew I didn't have the qualifications for; however, when God opens up a door He allows you to walk through them because what's for you is for you. I got the position, received a promotion, received a bonus of $10,000 and now an additional $8000 a year! Through this pandemic, God has been so good to me!

Due to my parents getting older, I moved them in with me and on March 24th, my mother was diagnosed with COVID-19. Due to my mother's underlining health issues, I feared COVID-19 would take my mom's life. Naturally, I thought my father and I would catch COVID-19 due to us sharing the same space. By the grace of God and being covered under the blood of Jesus Christ, we tested negative. Additionally, my mother was able to overcome the illness not having to be on a ventilator, nor did she experience the harsh symptoms of the disease. Now that she is negative, she has returned to doing the activities that bring joy and excitement into her life.

I remember walking in on my mom while she was praising God for her healing. She began sharing how she felt myself and my dad touching her body during the night… the truth is, my father nor myself was going in my mom's room during the middle of the night. We realized at that moment God sent His angels to touch my mom's body or He touched her Himself. God thought enough of my mom to personally get involved in her healing, what a God we serve.

We are a testimony that God can prevent you from getting illnesses and in the event, you do He can heal you… It's easy for Him… He is God and He loves you unconditionally.

Three times a day he would kneel down, pray, and give thanks to his God, just as he had previously done
Daniel 6:10 ISV

Day 67 Morning

Check all of your existing blessings:

☐ Health ☐ Shelter ☐ Food ☐ Clothing ☐ Family ☐ Life

In addition to the above, today I am grateful for...

Three times a day he would kneel down, pray, and give thanks to his God, just as he had previously done
Daniel 6:10 ISV

Day 67 Evening

As I close this day, I am truly Grateful for...

Write below anyone who blessed you with Kindness today.

-----------------------------------   -----------------------------------

-----------------------------------   -----------------------------------

-----------------------------------   -----------------------------------

How did you express to them your Gratitude?

Three times a day he would kneel down, pray, and give thanks to his God, just as he had previously done
Daniel 6:10 ISV

Day 68

Father,

Thank you for Healing in a mighty way. I went to the hospital for an outpatient surgery on my sinuses. After completing the surgery my doctor decided that I should stay overnight and leave in the morning. Morning came and the nurses came in and told me I can go home. As I began to get dressed, they went to get my discharge papers ready. When they left the room, I got up and went to the restroom, and about 15-20 minutes later, I woke up on the bathroom floor looking at the toilet... I passed out! What makes me so Grateful is the Supernatural Way God showed up and assisted me. During my unconsciousness, I recall walking on a dirt road with colorful flowers on each side of me! The amazing thing was there were thousands of butterflies with the same colors as the flowers; I could only see them when they were flying. I remember waking up woke smiling, but at the same time wondering why I was on the floor. By this time, the nurses came back and helped me in the bed.

I then learned I developed blood clots in my lungs during the surgery and that is what made me lose consciousness. Various specialists all over the hospital stated I should have died or at the least have some brain damage because my brain did not receive oxygen for 15-20 minutes. God you took me away to a place where I could escape death, until help came. I am grateful that God spared my life and I am grateful that He showed me that place that I have never seen anything like it in my life! Was it Heaven? I am not sure but it was beautiful and out of this world! For that, I AM GRATEFUL.

One of them, when he saw that he was healed, came back to Jesus, shouting, "Praise God!"
Luke 17:15 NLT

Day 68 Morning

Check all of your existing blessings:

☐ Health ☐ Shelter ☐ Food ☐ Clothing ☐ Family ☐ Life

In addition to the above, today I am grateful for...

One of them, when he saw that he was healed, came back to Jesus, shouting, "Praise God!"
Luke 17:15 NLT

Day 68 Evening

As I close this day, I am truly Grateful for...

Write below anyone who blessed you with Kindness today.

------------------------------------   ------------------------------------

------------------------------------   ------------------------------------

------------------------------------   ------------------------------------

How did you express to them your Gratitude?

One of them, when he saw that he was healed, came back to Jesus, shouting, "Praise God!"
Luke 17:15 NLT

Day 69

7 years ago, I had a 3-day born again experience that absolutely changed the course of my sails. Little did I know that over these past 7 years, God was building His temple within and transforming me back to my original kingdom DNA blueprints and restoring everything the enemy had stolen. And then some. This year alone during lockdown due to COVID, the Lord supernaturally healed ALL, not a few, but ALL of my infirmities that have had a death grip on me for too long. Since the devil can't have my heart and soul, he has tried to just kill me (since before I was born, my mother tried to commit suicide pregnant with me) through health issues, cancers, blood disease, emergency surgeries, and chronic pain. The old drug addiction didn't seem as rough (and it was BAD) compared to the grip on my well being and mental health that the enemy just tortured me through.

During these 7 years I have lost jobs, homes, cars, money, friendships, relationships with my children, my baby brother, and recently just two months ago, my heart and soul, my Daddy. I spent 3 of these 7 years fighting for my husband's soul in the realm and fighting against his pill addiction that Satan used to try and shred our marriage apart. I faced demonic entities daily and had I not fought and gone through 3 years of demonic oppression in my home, I would not have been able to crush his demons and save my household. My born-again anniversary date was October 1 and on that day something supernatural happened. The redecorating and restoration were completed. It was a moment where the Lord and I became one in such a way that I still struggle to find words to describe it. A lifetime of unworthiness, abuse, emotional and mental torture, then strictly walking and obeying the Lord these last 7 years in a way that others deemed me crazy, wrote me off, condemned me for, persecuted me for, and laughed at me for, paid off. The notebooks I have of incredible prophecy, not only personal, but direct from the Lord for others out there, will be used to help walk another through the pressing fire that is required to enter into the narrow door scripture talks about. I don't know how just yet it will get out into the world, I just know His promises have and continue to come true. I started a God's to Do List a few years ago right as the battle started to really shift gears and I can mark off pages and pages of prayers, pleas, wants, needs, and miracles that have come to fruition. Earlier this spring as COVID hit its peak, I was able to work from home as God had strategically planned, and if not daily, at least a few times a week, He supernaturally healed me from osteoarthritis, fibro, bi-polar disorder, a blood disease, acid reflux/hiatal hernia, digestive issues, chronic pain (I'd been on pain meds for years), nerve damage, neck and back issues (4-5 bulged discs and surgery was required in July 2020), manic thought patterns, unable to sleep, weight loss that I couldn't control, just to name a few. The day after my 7 year anniversary my Dad passed away and I had the opportunity to pray and war in the spirit for his soul where he received complete healing from a multitude of infirmities that held him captive. The Lord had to complete His temple and connect us as one before He could take my Daddy home with him. He knew I would not be able to survive such a loss.

The Lord ignited my assignment through the death of my Dad and just a few weeks ago I woke up and had noticed that I just looked different. I've put on a healthy amount of weight, I have a glory glow, and I have been off all medications since July/August of this year. The Lord also told me to retire my career in the corporate world in August and that I would never work under a corporate thumb again because I now work full time for the kingdom of heaven.

I still do not know what that looks like but I do have an idea of what is coming due to the prophecy that is written. He speaks directly to me, I have ears that see and eyes that hear, and the gift of prophecy, healing, and heaven follows me around unlike anything I've ever heard of. I woke up one day in September and all I could see was the fire of the Lion of Judah burning all around me. I get identified in public by the realm and death looks from people's demons within them. I was in strict isolation and hidden away in order for God to complete His agenda to prepare me and my body for the miracles that are coming for others to receive. This year alone has been an incredible journey. I am so grateful for the years of abuse, sleepless nights fighting demons, being rejected by others, losing everything in the natural to gain everything in the supernatural, all for the glory of God and to be able to carry the glory of the Lord.

Now thanks be unto God, which always causeth us to triumph in Christ
2 Corinthians 2:14 KJV

Day 69 Morning

Check all of your existing blessings:

☐ Health ☐ Shelter ☐ Food ☐ Clothing ☐ Family ☐ Life

In addition to the above, today I am grateful for...

Now thanks be unto God, which always causeth us to triumph in Christ
2 Corinthians 2:14 KJV

Day 69 Evening

As I close this day, I am truly Grateful for...

Write below anyone who blessed you with Kindness today.

------------------------------------   ------------------------------------

------------------------------------   ------------------------------------

------------------------------------   ------------------------------------

How did you express to them your Gratitude?

Now thanks be unto God, which always causeth us to triumph in Christ

2 Corinthians 2:14 KJV

Day 70

Jesus Christ,

Thank you for being an on-time God in all situations. For the past few days, a situation has been heavy on my heart. I needed to bring it express my feelings of betrayal to someone; however, I found myself wondering how to say it and when to say it. I decided to pray to you about it and I committed to trust and lean on your understanding versus my own. Lord, 24 hours later you provided the opportunity for me to share and the precise words to speak. Although I do not know what the outcome will be, I am truly grateful that I got it off my heart and now I can move forward without tha heavy load. Thank you for allowing me to bring all of my cares and concerns to you.

Thank you for answering when I call upon you.

All this is for your benefit, so that the grace that is reaching more and more people may cause thanksgiving to overflow to the glory of God.
2 Corinthians 4:15 NIV

Day 70 Morning

Check all of your existing blessings:

☐ Health ☐ Shelter ☐ Food ☐ Clothing ☐ Family ☐ Life

In addition to the above, today I am grateful for...

All this is for your benefit, so that the grace that is reaching more and more people may cause thanksgiving to overflow to the glory of God.
2 Corinthians 4:15 NIV

Day 70 Evening

As I close this day, I am truly Grateful for...

Write below anyone who blessed you with Kindness today.

------------------------------   ------------------------------

------------------------------   ------------------------------

------------------------------   ------------------------------

How did you express to them your Gratitude?

All this is for your benefit, so that the grace that is reaching more and more people may cause thanksgiving to overflow to the glory of God.
2 Corinthians 4:15 NIV

Day 71

Dear Lord,

You blessed me to pay my car off 8 months ago. I currently have 108,000 miles; however, I have never experienced any major problems with my vehicle. Today, my check engine light came on. I made contact with my mechanic and he got me in right away. After diagnosing the problem, he made the repairs and told me not to worry about any payment. Lord, I am forever grateful to you for the people you choose to bless me. Thank you for allowing my vehicle to be in good shape regardless of the miles. Additionally, I thank you for sparing me the financial burden of my vehicle repair.

Coming up to them at that very moment, she gave thanks to God
Luke 2:38 NIV

Day 71 Morning

Check all of your existing blessings:

☐ Health ☐ Shelter ☐ Food ☐ Clothing ☐ Family ☐ Life

In addition to the above, today I am grateful for...

Coming up to them at that very moment, she gave thanks to God
Luke 2:38 NIV

Day 71 Evening

As I close this day, I am truly Grateful for...

_____
_____
_____
_____
_____
_____
_____
_____
_____

Write below anyone who blessed you with Kindness today.

_____   _____

_____   _____

_____   _____

How did you express to them your Gratitude?

_____
_____
_____
_____
_____

Coming up to them at that very moment, she gave thanks to God
Luke 2:38 NIV

Day 72

Let me brag about my God!

God delivered me from a place of brokenness and insecurity and introduced me to my purpose. I grew up constantly being criticized by family members, never being told that I was good enough. I focused on gaining validation that would never come from them; I worried about how my life choices would affect their perception of me. Those feelings followed me into adulthood, where I struggled with approval addiction and constantly feeling the need to explain myself to others in order to feel validated. I wanted to live freely outside of the opinions of others, so I began to ask God to deliver me from approval addiction. It wasn't until I experienced a life-altering tragedy that I began to see those family members, those church members, and even a few friends for who they were: people who weren't attached to my destiny. God had to remind me that I'd placed so much hope in them, that it began to cloud my perception of Him. The same God who could deliver me from people was also the same God who could restore the brokenness of a 15-year old girl who never felt good enough, the young adult who was misunderstood by people who weren't meant to be in her life anyway, the woman who continued to hold on to expired relationships for the sake of history. He showed me that everything that I've ever been looking for has always been in Him; once I realized that, I saw myself for the first time. And for the first time, I can say that I love myself and I'm so proud of who I've become!

Devote yourselves to prayer, being watchful and thankful.
Colossians 4:2 NIV

Day 72 Morning

Check all of your existing blessings:

☐ Health ☐ Shelter ☐ Food ☐ Clothing ☐ Family ☐ Life

In addition to the above, today I am grateful for……………………………………

Devote yourselves to prayer, being watchful and thankful.
Colossians 4:2 NIV

Day 72 Evening

As I close this day, I am truly Grateful for...

Write below anyone who blessed you with Kindness today.

--   --

--   --

--   --

How did you express to them your Gratitude?

Devote yourselves to prayer, being watchful and thankful.
Colossians 4:2 NIV

Day 73

Heavenly father I am so grateful you allow my family to see this New Year. This past year I had complications with Gallbladder Surgery as well as Bacteria Pneumonia, yet you healed my body repeatedly. Even when certain medications received denials, you stepped in and those decisions were reversed. Lord, I thank you for my healing. I thank you God for my children who were there every step of the way. They attended doctor appointments, assisted financially, took care of the household and lifted me up in prayer until I was able to do for myself. Gracious God, I also thank you for an amazing church family and church leaders who interceded on my behalf. You said when prayers go up blessings come down. You provided for me new grace and mercy every day. Instead of having to go and seek employment, you blessed me to generate a salary from home by being the caregiver of my 89-year-old mother. Finally, I thank you for being God all by yourself; you saved my soul and cleaned me up in order to serve by you and your people. My prayer is that you continue working on me and break any chains of bondage on my life in Jesus name, Amen.

And he took a cup of wine and gave thanks to God for it.
Matthew 26:27 NLT

Day 73 Morning

Check all of your existing blessings:

☐ Health ☐ Shelter ☐ Food ☐ Clothing ☐ Family ☐ Life

In addition to the above, today I am grateful for...

And he took a cup of wine and gave thanks to God for it.
Matthew 26:27 NLT

Day 73 Evening

As I close this day, I am truly Grateful for………………………………………

Write below anyone who blessed you with Kindness today.

---------------------------------   ---------------------------------
---------------------------------   ---------------------------------
---------------------------------   ---------------------------------

How did you express to them your Gratitude?

And he took a cup of wine and gave thanks to God for it.
Matthew 26:27 NLT

Day 74

God
You have been so good! I launched a new home-based business in an industry that I purposely resisted. I prayed that you God would use me as a vessel to lead and financially empower people, as well as make a difference in their lives. Over the last 16 months, we have helped over 10 people retire from their jobs and spend more time with their family. We have also helped more people earn between $1000 and $5,000 additionally per month (part-time) from home than ever before. I thank you God for your mercy, grace and amazing blessings!

Joy and gladness will be found there. Songs of thanksgiving will fill the air.
Isaiah 51:3 NLT

Day 74 Morning

Check all of your existing blessings:

☐ Health ☐ Shelter ☐ Food ☐ Clothing ☐ Family ☐ Life

In addition to the above, today I am grateful for...

Joy and gladness will be found there. Songs of thanksgiving will fill the air.
Isaiah 51:3 NLT

Day 74 Evening

As I close this day, I am truly Grateful for...

Write below anyone who blessed you with Kindness today.

--------------------------------   --------------------------------
--------------------------------   --------------------------------
--------------------------------   --------------------------------

How did you express to them your Gratitude?

Joy and gladness will be found there. Songs of thanksgiving will fill the air.
Isaiah 51:3 NLT

Day 75

Hurt, Hate and Humility described who I was and what I felt. Hurt fueled my anger from relationships that betrayed me. Hate became friends with the bitterness from friendships that disappointed me. The humility came from shame, which encouraged hostility.

That was often my first impression.

I was seeking refuge in things, people and places that satisfied my hunger for peace only for seconds and never more than minutes. But God! I wanted to get up off my face, I needed to stand again, I was willing to do whatever it took to leave the darkness behind. God did it.

With a burning curiosity in my belly, I listened to prayer calls, I prayed, I sent in prayer request. I united in prayer with women from all over the world, who supported me and loved me. I learned how to pray, what to pray and how to apply the word of God to my life... Glory be to God, that hurt is now Hope, that Hate is now Happiness and humility is now Humanity. For those I proudly bless because I have been blessed. In Jesus name, I now serve from the overflow.

Praise and glory and wisdom and thanks and honor and power and strength be to our God for ever and ever. Amen!
Revelation 7:12 NIV

Day 75 Morning

Check all of your existing blessings:

☐ Health ☐ Shelter ☐ Food ☐ Clothing ☐ Family ☐ Life

In addition to the above, today I am grateful for..

Praise and glory and wisdom and thanks and honor and power and strength be to our God for ever and ever. Amen!
Revelation 7:12 NIV

Day 75 Evening

As I close this day, I am truly Grateful for..

Write below anyone who blessed you with Kindness today.

-------------------------------------   -------------------------------------
-------------------------------------   -------------------------------------
-------------------------------------   -------------------------------------

How did you express to them your Gratitude?

Praise and glory and wisdom and thanks and honor and power and strength be to our God for ever and ever. Amen!

Revelation 7:12 NIV

Day 76

Dear Jesus,

Psalms 37:25 says you the righteous will never be forsaken. For the past 5 years, my family has experienced tremendous financial decline. My husband and I have found ourselves unable to work due to disabilities. Although we receive disability checks, we haven't been able to catch up on all of our bills. Yesterday, it seemed like we hit rock bottom. I looked into our kitchen cabinets and refrigerator and found we were completely out of food. At this point, all I could do was cry out to you in sincere prayer. Today, Lord I went to the mailbox and found a much-needed blessing. We had received a check for a few hundred dollars. Lord today we were able to fill our cabinets and refrigerator. You may not have come when I wanted, but you were on time and you supplied our needs. Lord thank you for hearing my prayer and answering my cry. I am truly grateful.

I will offer to thee the sacrifice of thanksgiving, and will call upon the name of the LORD.
Psalm 116:17 KJV

Day 76 Morning

Check all of your existing blessings:

☐ Health ☐ Shelter ☐ Food ☐ Clothing ☐ Family ☐ Life

In addition to the above, today I am grateful for...

I will offer to thee the sacrifice of thanksgiving, and will call upon the name of the LORD.
Psalm 116:17 KJV

Day 76 Evening

As I close this day, I am truly Grateful for...

Write below anyone who blessed you with Kindness today.

------------------------------------   ------------------------------------

------------------------------------   ------------------------------------

------------------------------------   ------------------------------------

How did you express to them your Gratitude?

I will offer to thee the sacrifice of thanksgiving, and will call upon the name of the LORD.

Psalm 116:17 KJV

Day 77

As this year comes to a close I want to make sure that I take some time to let you know how thankful I am for your goodness and mercy. I faced my biggest challenges this year and I feel that you truly showed your presence in my life through it all.

I specifically want to thank you for a series of events that happened in my life in which you were truly the Great Conductor that navigated me through the storms. **At the age of just 44, fit and well to do, I had three strokes within 24 hours.**

At the time of my first stroke, I didn't realize I was having a stroke. I was on the road driving, your grace allowed me to make it home without injuring myself or others. My second stroke I was at home with my son and he was able to call 911. It was your set time when the third stroke hit me, I was in the presence of healthcare providers who were able to administer medication and immediately address the crisis. As I write today, I have returned to my regular life routine. I am now a spokesperson for the medical facility, and I encourage other stroke patients in their recovery. Lord, if I had a thousand tongues I couldn't thank you enough for your love, your grace, your mercy, and unmerited strokes of Favor in my life. In Jesus name, Thank you my Heavenly Father!

Be strong in the faith, just as you were taught, and always be thankful.
Colossians 2:7 NCV

Day 77 Morning

Check all of your existing blessings:

☐ Health   ☐ Shelter   ☐ Food   ☐ Clothing   ☐ Family   ☐ Life

In addition to the above, today I am grateful for...

Be strong in the faith, just as you were taught, and always be thankful.
Colossians 2:7 NCV

Day 77 Evening

As I close this day, I am truly Grateful for...

Write below anyone who blessed you with Kindness today.

-------------------------------------   -------------------------------------
-------------------------------------   -------------------------------------
-------------------------------------   -------------------------------------

How did you express to them your Gratitude?

Be strong in the faith, just as you were taught, and always be thankful.
Colossians 2:7 NCV

Day 78

Heavenly Father!

Thank you, thank you, thank you for being faithful to me. This has been a wavering school year for my child. Some of the subjects were difficult to comprehend and test taking was intimidating. As a result, his grades were failing. I have been praying for him this entire year, believing you would help. I want to thank you because things are turning around for the better. Grades are improving and his comprehension is improving. Today, I attended an event at his school and to my total surprise his name was listed on the "Wall of Honor Student." Because of your grace, mercy and love, my child went from failing to being recognized as an honor student. Thank you for your amazing power.

And you will joyfully give thanks to the Father who has made you
Colossians 1:12 NCV

Day 78 Morning

Check all of your existing blessings:

☐ Health ☐ Shelter ☐ Food ☐ Clothing ☐ Family ☐ Life

In addition to the above, today I am grateful for...

And you will joyfully give thanks to the Father who has made you
Colossians 1:12 NCV

Day 78 Evening

As I close this day, I am truly Grateful for...

Write below anyone who blessed you with Kindness today.

------------------------------------   ------------------------------------

------------------------------------   ------------------------------------

------------------------------------   ------------------------------------

How did you express to them your Gratitude?

And you will joyfully give thanks to the Father who has made you
Colossians 1:12 NCV

Day 79

Dear God,

Thank you for blessing me to achieve a personal and educational goal. My desire was to become a Life Coach and assist people with bringing their goals and dreams into reality. You blessed me with the money to pay for my certification classes. I'm grateful that I successfully completed my course and I am a Certified Professional Life Coach. Thank you Jesus for providing the resources I needed to succeed.

Let us be thankful and please God by worshiping him with holy fear and awe.
Hebrews 12:28 NLT

Day 79 Morning

Check all of your existing blessings:

☐ Health ☐ Shelter ☐ Food ☐ Clothing ☐ Family ☐ Life

In addition to the above, today I am grateful for……………………………………………

Let us be thankful and please God by worshiping him with holy fear and awe.
Hebrews 12:28 NLT

Day 79 Evening

As I close this day, I am truly Grateful for...

\---

\---

\---

\---

\---

\---

\---

\---

\---

\---

Write below anyone who blessed you with Kindness today.

\-------------------------------------   \-------------------------------------

\-------------------------------------   \-------------------------------------

\-------------------------------------   \-------------------------------------

How did you express to them your Gratitude?

\---

\---

\---

\---

\---

\---

Let us be thankful and please God by worshiping him with holy fear and awe.
Hebrews 12:28 NLT

Day 80

Dear Jehovah Nissi,

You have truly been my banner, providing me mental and emotional victory today. Lord, I recently brought to you a concern that was dear to my heart. Although I gave it over to you, I found myself picking it up due to worry and fear. Lord, you provided a revelation that gave me freedom from worry and fear. Lord, you showed me how to defeat worry and fear by having Faith and Trust in you. You instructed me not to worry about the past because I cannot change it and not to fear the future because I cannot predict it. Additionally, you blessed me to hear a sermon by Pastor Chuck Swindoll that gave greater clarity and instruction. From the sermon, I learned: 1. God has already predetermined my race. I did not determine my journey, God determined it and He is in full control of my life. 2. I am responsible for preparing for the race God has for me. This means I must rid myself of any excess weight such as negativity, worry, fear and procrastination and unbelief. 3. I am to keep running my race to the end faithfully; it is not about speed but endurance. 4. Stay focused on Jesus Christ throughout the race. Turn my attention away from the distractions. 5. Refuse to concern myself with the past. 6. Strive towards the finish line 7. Never forget that my rewards await me.

I will praise the Lord at all times; his praise is always on my lips.
Psalms 34:1 NCV

Day 80 Morning

Check all of your existing blessings:

☐ Health ☐ Shelter ☐ Food ☐ Clothing ☐ Family ☐ Life

In addition to the above, today I am grateful for...

I will praise the Lord at all times; his praise is always on my lips.
Psalms 34:1 NCV

Day 80 Evening

As I close this day, I am truly Grateful for...

Write below anyone who blessed you with Kindness today.

---------------------------------------   ---------------------------------------
---------------------------------------   ---------------------------------------
---------------------------------------   ---------------------------------------

How did you express to them your Gratitude?

I will praise the Lord at all times; his praise is always on my lips.
Psalms 34:1 NCV

Day 81

Gracious Father,

Most recently, I experienced a very frightening situation at the end of my workday everyone was gone home. Being tired and exhausted I got on the elevator instead of taking the stairs as I normally do. There are only two floors. I pushed the button after the door closed to go to the first floor. After a minute, I noticed that the elevator was not moving. I began to panic and started pushing buttons; nothing happened. I said let me calm my spirit so I would not to have a panic attack. After taking some deep breaths, I reached for the emergency phone; told the man what was happening and he too encouraged me to calm down and follow his instructions, which should release the door. I did; but nothing happened. I began to feel very phobic; started sweating and began praying to myself saying "God, please help me in this crisis moment." I tried not to think about all that could have happened to me in that closed-door phobic situation. Having my cell phone, finally, I was able to get in contact with someone who would need to go upstairs to open the door manually. I kept taking deep breaths; and said to God again, "please help me." I again began to follow the directions of the emergency contact person; held the button 10 seconds; and the elevator door began to open; way before the person could open it manually. I know what prayer will do. Prayer will see you through. Without a fear of contradiction, I can truly say God Does Open Doors. Lord, I want to thank you for making a way out of no way!

I give you thanks, O LORD, with my whole heart; before the gods I sing your praise
Psalm 138:1 ESV

Day 81 Morning

Check all of your existing blessings:

☐ Health ☐ Shelter ☐ Food ☐ Clothing ☐ Family ☐ Life

In addition to the above, today I am grateful for...

I give you thanks, O LORD, with my whole heart; before the gods I sing your praise
Psalm 138:1 ESV

Day 81 Evening

As I close this day, I am truly Grateful for...

Write below anyone who blessed you with Kindness today.

-------------------------------------   -------------------------------------
-------------------------------------   -------------------------------------
-------------------------------------   -------------------------------------

How did you express to them your Gratitude?

I give you thanks, O LORD, with my whole heart; before the gods I sing your praise
Psalm 138:1 ESV

Day 82

Dear God,

You have been such a powerful force in my life! Over the past few years, I have been more in tune to just how great you are. I never have to look too far back to see just how present you are in my life.

I have been working on getting things in order in my life and during the process, it has been challenging but I have managed to stay the course and do the best I can. Most recently, I went into a situation that was NOT perfect...in fact in the natural it was very flawed, and I found myself really having to exercise my faith like never before. While I knew that, you God could work it out for me I will be honest in saying that I wondered if you would do it for me.

Long story short, I kept speaking life and what I envisioned for myself regarding this matter, in spite of what I knew to be true and how I felt. God, you showed up and out for me like only The Father could! You gave me amazing grace and favor in the midst of my messiness simply to show me that you are always in control!

What I really discovered in that moment is that when I wrote the vision, spoke God's promises and stayed in faith, My Savior, will show up faithful as always will bring to pass the desires of my heart. Jesus, you have blown my mind so much so that I have no choice but to acknowledge you and say, "God did it!" In addition, I was reminded that I must let God be God in every situation no matter what!

We always thank God for all of you and pray for you constantly.
1 Thessalonians 1:2 NLT

Day 82 Morning

Check all of your existing blessings:

☐ Health ☐ Shelter ☐ Food ☐ Clothing ☐ Family ☐ Life

In addition to the above, today I am grateful for...

We always thank God for all of you and pray for you constantly.
1 Thessalonians 1:2 NLT

Day 82 Evening

As I close this day, I am truly Grateful for...

Write below anyone who blessed you with Kindness today.

-------------------------------------   -------------------------------------
-------------------------------------   -------------------------------------
-------------------------------------   -------------------------------------

How did you express to them your Gratitude?

We always thank God for all of you and pray for you constantly.
1 Thessalonians 1:2 NLT

Day 83

Dear Prayer Answering Father,

Thank you for the blessing you had awaiting me when I arrived home. A few months ago, my 2-year-old daughter was in need of emergency surgery. Although we had insurance, my out of pocket expense was going to be $3000. I accepted the terms and prayed for y our assistance for the balance. I applied for economic hardship in order to reduce my out of pocket expense. My $3000 bill reduced to $900. I decided to make payment arrangements. Prior to my first payment, my $900 bill reduced again, now it was $200. While at work, I was in the process of paying the bill, you Lord spoke to me and said, "Wait." I obeyed. When I arrived home and opened my mail. I found your blessing. My bill reduced a final time to $50! How amazing it that! I have now paid my bill in full. Thank for answering my prayer and saving me $2500.00.

Every king in all the earth will thank you, LORD, for all of them will hear your words.
Psalm 138:4 NLT

Day 83 Morning

Check all of your existing blessings:

☐ Health ☐ Shelter ☐ Food ☐ Clothing ☐ Family ☐ Life

In addition to the above, today I am grateful for……………………………………………

Every king in all the earth will thank you, LORD, for all of them will hear your words.
Psalm 138:4 NLT

Day 83 Evening

As I close this day, I am truly Grateful for..

Write below anyone who blessed you with Kindness today.

------------------------------------   ------------------------------------

------------------------------------   ------------------------------------

------------------------------------   ------------------------------------

How did you express to them your Gratitude?

Every king in all the earth will thank you, LORD, for all of them will hear your words.
Psalm 138:4 NLT

Day 84

Lord, I start not just on this day but every day, thanking you for the gift of being a mom. I know not everyone get to experience the ability to give birth to a child, so I am wonderfully and graciously thankful for you choosing me to give birth to two beautiful children. I understand the ultimate responsibility this role entails and take none of it for granted. I know part of the lesson learned from you calling my mother home was for me to be all that I can be to my children for I know not the day or the hour you will call me home.

I am thankful because I decided to strengthen myself in areas of my life and begin the journey of true commitment and development of my children. I started recognizing the qualities that needed to be invested in their lives physically, intellectually and most importantly spiritually. I made a vow that I would show them at a young age how to clean, cook, pray, study and care genuinely for others. I did not have any specific instructions, but I did have your word, which says in Proverbs 22:6, Train up a child in the way he should go, and when he is old, he will not depart from it. I took this scripture, prayer and the village which you strategically placed in my life and started the process. I am sometimes in awe of your glory, your blessings and your faithfulness to my children and me. I can truly testify that your word is true.

I thank you for all the experiences this journey has brought so far and Lord I am thanking you in advance for what is yet to come. There is no greater love than you dying for my sins and the love a mother has for her children. These beautiful gifts often teach me so many lessons through the lives they are living. Thank you, Lord, thank you Lord, I just want to thank you Lord. I am an abundantly blessed Mother!

If you want to offer some special offering of thanks to the Lord, you must do it in a way that pleases him.
Leviticus 22:29 NCV

Day 84 Morning

Check all of your existing blessings:

☐ Health ☐ Shelter ☐ Food ☐ Clothing ☐ Family ☐ Life

In addition to the above, today I am grateful for...

If you want to offer some special offering of thanks to the Lord, you must do it in a way that pleases him.
Leviticus 22:29 NCV

Day 84 Evening

As I close this day, I am truly Grateful for...

_____

_____

_____

_____

_____

_____

_____

_____

_____

Write below anyone who blessed you with Kindness today.

_____   _____

_____   _____

_____   _____

How did you express to them your Gratitude?

_____

_____

_____

_____

_____

_____

If you want to offer some special offering of thanks to the Lord, you must do it in a way that pleases him.
Leviticus 22:29 NCV

Day 85

Dear Lord,
Thank you for saving my home from destruction. This morning, I started my day in prayer, which is my regular daily routine. As I walked into my prayer area, I realized I left my candle burning from the day before. I immediately felt a funny feeling in my stomach because I knew anything could have happened during the 24 hours the candle burned in the lower level of my home. My family went to work and school, enjoyed family time when we returned home and slept, not knowing the candle was burning downstairs. Lord, our city has had numerous house fires over the past weeks, leaving families homeless. Lord, this could have easily been our situation due to my negligence. I am grateful Lord you intervened in our affairs and protected or home from ruin. Thank you for looking past my fault and extending your Grace and Mercy. Jesus, I sincerely thank you.

To stand every morning to thank and praise the Lord, and likewise at evening
1 Chronicles 23:30 NKJV

Day 85 Morning

Check all of your existing blessings:

☐ *Health* ☐ *Shelter* ☐ *Food* ☐ *Clothing* ☐ *Family* ☐ *Life*

In addition to the above, today I am grateful for...

To stand every morning to thank and praise the Lord, and likewise at evening
1 Chronicles 23:30 NKJV

Day 85 Evening

As I close this day, I am truly Grateful for...

Write below anyone who blessed you with Kindness today.

------------------------------------   ------------------------------------
------------------------------------   ------------------------------------
------------------------------------   ------------------------------------

How did you express to them your Gratitude?

To stand every morning to thank and praise the Lord, and likewise at evening
1 Chronicles 23:30 NKJV

Day 86

I am grateful to experience and know that God Is Love

Beloved, let us love one another, for love is from God, and whoever loves has been born of God and knows God. Anyone who does not love does not know God, because God is love. 1 John 4:7-8

Have you ever found yourself feeling alone, sad, depressed, and no one in the world knows how you feel because each day you do an amazing job convincing other you happy? Well I know exactly how that feels. I found myself unhappy at work, unhappy at home, unhappy in my marriage and ultimately felt unloved. To be completely transparent I did not love myself. Completely exhausted with life I had given up on the very promise God gives, His love. In the moment I had completely given up I cried out to God and said I feel so unloved, not through my words but through my tears as I cried. That's when God showed me just how much I was loved. Neighbors, family, friends, near and far literally started reaching out to visit, called, and random gifts of kindness began showing up. Flowers, edible arrangements, random text with "I love you" staggered in each day. This was God's way of reminding me God is love. He hears our heart and tears and loves us even when we forget to love ourselves. Thank you, God, for reminding me of your promise.

Therefore will I give thanks unto thee, O LORD, among the heathen, and sing praises unto thy name.
Psalm 18:49 KJV

Day 86 Morning

Check all of your existing blessings:

☐ Health ☐ Shelter ☐ Food ☐ Clothing ☐ Family ☐ Life

In addition to the above, today I am grateful for...

Therefore will I give thanks unto thee, O LORD, among the heathen, and sing praises unto thy name.
Psalm 18:49 KJV

Day 86 Evening

As I close this day, I am truly Grateful for...

Write below anyone who blessed you with Kindness today.

-------------------------------------   -------------------------------------
-------------------------------------   -------------------------------------
-------------------------------------   -------------------------------------

How did you express to them your Gratitude?

Therefore will I give thanks unto thee, O LORD, among the heathen, and sing praises unto thy name.
Psalm 18:49 KJV

Day 87

Lord, I thank you for taking me from tragedy to triumph! After an extremely complicated pregnancy, I gave birth to a 1-lbs.14-ounce premature little girl. I sincerely had great expectation of my daughter making it through her complications and living a healthy life, however; July , I had to bury my little angel. God, I thank you for carrying me through and keeping me strong, even when I thought I wanted to die after burying my child. On top of this, I found my four sons and myself homeless. God you blessed us with the ability to rotate between the homes of great family and friends.

In August, Lord, you blessed me with a job. Although my family was still homeless, I went to work because I decided that you would get the glory, honor and praise. This test would become a testimony for you Jesus.

After six months on the job, I was promoted to store manager over a store that was deemed unproductive. Lord, I had fear of this promotion because I knew my job depended on improving production of this store, however, I listened to a sweet little lady that reminded me it's going to work out and trust God like you've been doing. Sure enough, you worked it out Father; my store was doing great, every month the numbers grew.

I entered a temporary homeless program for a few months. They helped get evictions off my record and helped get my truck fixed. Although the program did not last long, it did what you needed it to do. Even though we are homeless again, I am not worried or scared. This journey has brought my children and me closer. Together, we seek you for guidance and I know everything is going to be o.k.

In September, I started getting my check garnished; however, you told me to relax, stay calm and do not worry. After 3 months of garnishments, I began receiving unexpected checks in the mail and each week they increased. Jesus, I later found out these checks were refunds of the garnishments. WOW JESUS!

Today, a new home is being prepared for my boys and me! We move in early February! Lord throughout this journey, you have kept your love and faithfulness towards me and my family. I have not always been a great person or even a good person. I have done some horrible things and been through some terrible things, but God, you made it possible and saw fit to keep my family safe. For this, I am thankful, and I am able to smile. It could have been worse. I am not where I want to be, but I am where you want me to be Lord. At this moment, I trust you at your word and I sincerely trust your plan for us. To God be the Glory!

Praise the LORD. Give thanks to the LORD, for he is good; his love endures forever.
Psalm 106:1 NIV

Day 87 Morning

Check all of your existing blessings:

☐ Health   ☐ Shelter   ☐ Food   ☐ Clothing   ☐ Family   ☐ Life

In addition to the above, today I am grateful for…………………………………………

Praise the LORD. Give thanks to the LORD, for he is good; his love endures forever.
Psalm 106:1 NIV

Day 87 Evening

As I close this day, I am truly Grateful for...

Write below anyone who blessed you with Kindness today.

---------------------------------   ---------------------------------

---------------------------------   ---------------------------------

---------------------------------   ---------------------------------

How did you express to them your Gratitude?

Praise the LORD. Give thanks to the LORD, for he is good; his love endures forever.
Psalm 106:1 NIV

Day 88

Dear God,

Thank you for the uncommon financial blessing you gave me today. A young woman hit my car from behind and damaged the entire back end of my car. Additionally, my face hit the steering wheel and I suffered minor disfigurement. After exchange insurance information and me pursuing her insurance for repairs, I was notified her policy elapsed and I would be responsible for my own repairs and medical treatment. My insurance company informed me they would be paying for the repairs to my vehicle; however, because I did not have medical insurance attached to my policy. During this time, I received a $7000 bill from the hospital. After speaking with a representative from the hospital, she reduced my bill to less than $1500. This was my first blessing. To my surprise, I received a call from my insurance company stating that I had uninsured and underinsured motorist on my policy and because of this, all of my expenses due to the accident fall within my policy for full coverage plus extra for pain and suffering. In the end, I walked away with over $14,000, excluding the cost for my vehicle repairs. This was my second blessing. Lord, I thank you for working this out for my good. You turned potential tragedy to triumph.

Let them thank the LORD for his steadfast love, for his wondrous works to the children of man!
Psalm 107:8 ESV

Day 88 Morning

Check all of your existing blessings:

☐ *Health* ☐ *Shelter* ☐ *Food* ☐ *Clothing* ☐ *Family* ☐ *Life*

In addition to the above, today I am grateful for...

Let them thank the LORD for his steadfast love, for his wondrous works to the children of man!
Psalm 107:8 ESV

Day 88 Evening

As I close this day, I am truly Grateful for...

_____

_____

_____

_____

_____

_____

_____

_____

_____

Write below anyone who blessed you with Kindness today.

_____   _____

_____   _____

_____   _____

How did you express to them your Gratitude?

_____

_____

_____

_____

_____

_____

Let them thank the LORD for his steadfast love, for his wondrous works to the children of man!
Psalm 107:8 ESV

Day 89

Dear Lord,

I come to you on today thanking you for answering my prayer. I remember praying and believing You for a better job, house and car. I received a job, but I knew that was not all You had in store for me. I continued to pray and thank You for what was to come. After working for six months at my new job on my birthday I was called into an office. I was advised there would be a layoff but that I was safe from the layoff and would receive a $20k raise added to my annual salary. I was so thankful to God and his continued blessings.

O give thanks unto the LORD; for he is good: for his mercy endureth for ever.
Psalm 118:29 KJV

Day 89 Morning

Check all of your existing blessings:

☐Health ☐ Shelter ☐ Food ☐ Clothing ☐ Family ☐ Life

In addition to the above, today I am grateful for...

O give thanks unto the LORD; for he is good: for his mercy endureth for ever.
Psalm 118:29 KJV

Day 89 Evening

As I close this day, I am truly Grateful for...

Write below anyone who blessed you with Kindness today.

-------------------------------------   -------------------------------------

-------------------------------------   -------------------------------------

-------------------------------------   -------------------------------------

How did you express to them your Gratitude?

O give thanks unto the LORD; for he is good: for his mercy endureth for ever.
Psalm 118:29 KJV

Day 90

My testament of God's love reaches way back when I was a little girl feeling rejected and alone. I can remember my Sunday school teacher teaching us the song 'He's got the whole world in his hands' Singing that song I cried at 7 years old with the words 'He's got the mother and father in his hands' somehow peace came over me and I knew he would make it alright. God's love has given me hope on my darkest days. I can remember being in so much emotional pain from relationship that I cried out to God to take the pain away, and he did. Little by little. He took up residence in my heart and showed me that he was all I needed. I have been restored through the word of God, scripture by scripture; application by faith. God has been so good to me. I walk on purpose on purpose. I have a beautiful family, and loving husband and a talents and gifts too many to count. I am abundantly blessed. Some things I'm still waiting on but praise God they are on the way! My hope is in Jesus! That's my testament of faith. That's my testimony of how he's brought me out and how he's bringing me through. There is absolutely nothing I can't do and deal with walking in Christ! I am walking to my victory whether I'm on the mountain top or valley low. He's got me for he's got the whole world in his hands!

Be thankful in all circumstances, for this is God's will for you who belong to Christ Jesus.
1 Thessalonians 5:18 NLT

Day 90 Morning

Check all of your existing blessings:

☐ Health ☐ Shelter ☐ Food ☐ Clothing ☐ Family ☐ Life

In addition to the above, today I am grateful for...

Be thankful in all circumstances, for this is God's will for you who belong to Christ Jesus.
1 Thessalonians 5:18 NLT

Day 90 Evening

As I close this day, I am truly Grateful for...

Write below anyone who blessed you with Kindness today.

--   --
--   --
--   --

How did you express to them your Gratitude?

Be thankful in all circumstances, for this is God's will for you who belong to Christ Jesus.
1 Thessalonians 5:18 NLT

Author Thank You

God trusted me with an assignment to help in the building of His Kingdom on Earth. He stated the purpose of this gratitude journal was to open up the eyes of His people to the daily benefits and blessings He bestows on us daily and that our recognition and gratefulness of his blessings would open the door for so much more in our lives. This daily activity of journaling our blessings would not only create grateful hearts, but it would cause us, His Children to come to Him more often in prayer. It is with great humility and gratitude; I thank my Lord and Savior Jesus Christ for pouring into me His inspiration, spirit and wisdom to accomplish this amazing task. Jesus, I thank you for releasing every resource, as it needed. Lord there is nothing greater than working for You because only what I do for You, will last.

From the depth of my heart, Thank you to the phenomenal contributors comprised of family, friends, co-workers, neighbors and church members who caught the vision of this assignment and shared their transparent testimonials of how God took them from tragedy to triumph, brokenness to breakthroughs, terrifying test to testimonies and their mess into miracles! Thank you for letting your light so shine before men, that they may see your good works, and glorify your Father which is in heaven. My prayer is that God bless you and your family beyond your wildest dreams.

Thank you to my awesome husband who blindly supported me throughout this journey. Many occasions I had to decline activities in order to complete this assignment, but you never complained. I am grateful for your patience and understanding. You have inspired me in many ways to be the woman God has called me to be. I love you and I Thank you.

Thank you to my children (Mujahid, Mia, Marquita and Marina), grandchildren and great-grandchildren! You all are so precious, and you light up my world. Each of you are added blessings to my life. Thank you for the many hug, kisses and outpouring of love you show unconditionally. There are no words to express your value to me. I love you all.

Thank you to everyone who sacrificed their time to pray on my behalf and this assignment. God heard and answered you! Thank you for your kind words, encouragement and support. You all are amazing!

Lastly, to my Grandmother Ethel, Sister Sharrae and Brother Ontaria, Spiritual Mom Tamera and Best Friend Michelle, I can never thank God enough for you all. You all have been my strength when I was weak and my smile when I was sad. Likewise, you all have celebrated by greatest victories. No matter what my life journey has encompassed, I have always known you are in my corner. Thank you for being my family and biggest cheerleaders. I love you from the depth of my heart.

Author Bio

Dynamic, authentic, strategic and caring are words clients have used to describe LaShonda Lee. LaShonda Lee is a Wife, Mother, Author, Coach and business owner who is fiercely committed to helping women who struggle with getting unstuck discover resilience so they can own their brilliance. She's passionate about guiding women into making good life choices, taking action towards their dreams and stepping into a sassy and classy life they control and live on their terms.

For many years, she has been actively involved as a mentor, leader and motivational speaker helping others establish and achieve their spiritual, personal and professional goals.

In 2014, LaShonda was also called to ministry. She is the wife of Rev. David Lee and serves as First Lady and Co-Women Ministry Leader of Guiding Star Missionary Baptist Church. LaShonda is a much sought-after spiritual speaker, teacher and trainer, specializing in teaching individuals how to be the best version of themselves and exemplify how to boldly walk into the destiny God has already planned for them. LaShonda is obedient to her call and ministers wherever God sends her. She cherishes her ability to connect with individuals and help them see the seeds of greatness God has planted within them.

Connect with LaShonda:

Website: www.walkinfavoirnc.com

Email: LaShonda@walkinfavorinc.com

Facebook: www.facebook.com/lashondaslee

Facebook: www.facebook.com/walkinfavorinc

Instagram: @lamlashondalee

Twitter: @walkinfavor

Made in the USA
Las Vegas, NV
22 September 2021